CAPTAIN KAMPER AND THE
BURST OF FLAME

CAPTAIN KAMPER AND THE BURST OF FLAME

RICHARD MOLLOWEN

© Richard Mollowen, 2020

Published by Skrallkit Publishing

A CIP catalogue record for this book is available from the British Library.

ISBN 978-1-9996980-3-4

Book layout and cover design by Clare Brayshaw

Cover background image   © Aleksandar Mijatovic | Dreamstime.com
© Dmitri Afanasec | Dreamstime.com

Prepared and printed by:

York Publishing Services Ltd

64 Hallfield Road
Layerthorpe
York YO31 7ZQ

Tel: 01904 431213

Website: www.yps-publishing.co.uk

For my daughters

In memoriam:

Cyril, Bob, Cliff, Jack and Wuff

to the Muse

Contents

Preface ix

Prologue xiii

Part One – The Setting Forth

Chapter 1 1

Chapter 2 9

Chapter 3 13

Chapter 4 18

Chapter 5 22

Chapter 6 28

Chapter 7 30

Part Two – Ship of Fools

Chapter 8 39

Part Three – Northern Spain; Southern France

Chapter 9 49

Chapter 10 54

Chapter 11 61

Part Four – Italy – mainland

Chapter 12 69

Chapter 13 78

Chapter 14 85

Chapter 15 93

Chapter 16 102

Chapter 17   106

Chapter 18   115

Chapter 19   118

Chapter 20   124

Chapter 21   131

Chapter 22   135

Chapter 23   138

Chapter 24   142

Part Five – Italy – Sicilia

Chapter 25   151

Chapter 26   163

Chapter 27   171

Chapter 28   175

Chapter 29   182

Chapter 30   190

Chapter 31   194

Chapter 32   200

Chapter 33   209

Chapter 34   221

Chapter 35   224

Part Six – Come Back to Sorrento

Chapter 36   231

Chapter 37   234

Chapter 38   241

Chapter 39   247

Chapter 40   252

Chapter 41   256

Chapter 42   260

Chapter 43   265

Acknowledgements   272

Preface

This is, I'm afraid, a book that will be hard to categorise, in a bookshop or on your shelves.

It's a travel book: by camper-van. It's a personal memoir, thinly-disguised, which might in turn lead some to say that actually, it's a novel. It's a grubbed-up history of a man (my father) especially in the Desert Air Force in World War II. It's about family: and the story of a wedding – my second daughter Laura's. It's obsessed with volcanoes and other explosive things. It's about Italy, including Sicily, from the late 19th Century onwards and up to 2010.

However: I'm an ageing literature student, not really a historian of Fascism and the war against it; I know little about volcanoes and less about explosives; my family were and are lovely people, and not (apart from me) particularly idiosyncratic; and my Dad, a gentle, quiet man, actually told us very little about "his" war. As for Travel – well at times, such is the miasma of consciousness which passes here for narration, the landscape and culture of present-day Italy will often be barely visible.

I'm really selling this, aren't I?

It would be good to say that it all began with reading "Travels with Charley", John Steinbeck's seminal road-book, in my late teens – but that too is *almost* a pretentious claim. It might be more honest to begin with earlier childhood reading: "Five Go Off In A Caravan"; "The World Of The Children" (a 1950s Children's Encyclopaedia in four big volumes); and of course, "Biggles Sweeps The Desert".

After that, there loomed a great deal more, and much more worthy, literature, but not before "The Dambusters", a great deal of pubescent Airfix modelling, and skims of biographies such as Leonard Cheshire's – and *then* "Charley". By the time I'd completed my degree in English Language and

Literature, I knew I was more interested in history and biography than in the Great Tradition.

What finally won out here, so that this book had to be written eventually, was a stubborn old back-story of childhood dreams and nightmares. This demanded, at last, a travel through the Encyclopedia in my own caravan, rattling south through clouds of dust and ashes. Everyone knows: the Journey is always the Story, and *vice versa*.

Maybe – it did become a classic – you will have read "Travels With Charley"? But Steinbeck's literary star, notwithstanding such fine novels as "Of Mice and Men" and "The Grapes of Wrath", has fallen pretty considerably since those days, so it's possible you haven't. "Travels with Charley – in Search of America". Gentle, restrained, elegiac as it is, I read that very first of all camper-van books at a time when "shades of the prison-house" were already beginning to close. Still, somehow it crawled into a back corner of a difficult brain: a vague, persistent reassurance that one day, maybe, a trip might be undertaken that in turn might eventually, windingly, lead to the writing of a book. But when? A dream of a dream.

John Steinbeck and Charley, Sag Harbour, New York, 1960

My hero's travels, though, while technically they cover a couple more "countries" than Steinbeck's, are more small-scale than the great man's, and relatively-local – UK and European.

My 'Captain' wears no nautical headgear – but he's seen campervan-drivers who do... He dislikes dogs – unless they belong to others. His van isn't a one-off commission like the Quixotic Nobel-Winner's "Rocinante": it's a seventeen-year-old German Hymermobil 550S – so left-hand drive of course – one of thousands built in 1992; this example bought as an import in 2005 from a dealer in Huddersfield. The van's name is Lotte; but that's only because people since well before Steinbeck have felt that certain vehicles and beasts of burden need anthropomorphizing – and the Captain doesn't like to disappoint.

The book you hold now is, like "Charley", about a time-of-life, at least as much as it's about the times we live in, or about places visited, or about Travel. My Captain knows as he travels: that his own country of Britain is becoming almost as foreign to him these days as the rest of the continent of Europe. Unlike his towering predecessor, for some weeks of his travels he'll gladly finds himself adrift upon a sea of languages and cultures with which he has, on the face of it, minimal connection, and in countries where there's little danger of hearing his own tongue spoken by anyone he meets.

He'll travel to Italy, to make sense of himself through visiting (The Past) some war-time places of his father's and (Present and Future) to "give away" in marriage one of his daughters. Maybe aping Steinbeck, he will mostly travel alone, leaving partner and offspring at home (well, in their various homes) though like JS he'll try to arrange some careful *rendez-vous* with folks so that they can share parts of his journey.

Finally, this Captain knows, just as the escaping Laureate did, that back home he has

"too many THINGS".

Oh, and also like Steinbeck in 1960, he's noticed, in 2010, that he's 58 years old. Maybe there's something, too, about that age.

Additional sources will be noted, I hope accurately, within or at the foot of the text as we go.

Finally. Ahem.

I must acknowledge that there have always been those around me who have wished that I were more present – and not just when I'm physically absent, but when here at home, and now. I owe a huge debt of gratitude to the love and patience of my nearest and dearest. You know who you are.

Leeds, May 2020

Prologue

It matters not how strait the gate,

How charged with punishments the scroll,

I am the master of my fate:

I am the captain of my soul.

W.E. Henley, 'Life and Death Echoes', 1875

2005. "The Captain" is Commissioned

He's standing at the main entrance, in front of Reception. It's the day of his retirement from this place.

July. Late afternoon sun slants in. He braces himself for his boss's Few Kind Words, for the little presentation, and his own short speech, mostly jokes, folded in his inside pocket.

He stares out through plate-glass doors at the car-park, hedges and council flats beyond. A delivery-van-man, about his own age he'll guess, and full of similar vigour, now almost trots in through the doors – it's probably the last drop of the week – leaves a couple of boxes of printer-paper by the office-door and asks him to sign the chitty. He does so, prints his job-role as required by the docket, and looks at it a moment longer than normal.

The feller takes the pad back, and the pencil. Then in the facetious style of certain men of a certain age to others momentarily apprehended as 'alike', he cracks out a brisk, "Thanks, Captain".

And out again he scoots to his wagon. It re-starts with a big, bold grunt of diesel, a jolt of gear, and is gone, except for the flavour of drifting exhaust.

The man standing by the glowing sunset exit smiles to himself. Making a mental note that – Yes, he definitely will buy that old motorhome he saw last week – he turns with sudden urgency to say his official goodbyes.

2006 Mid-April

Sometimes there's nowhere in the world so wet as a Herefordshire caravan-site in April.

No matter how leak-proof and sleek your new caravan, and how sturdy your awning, you're under the thumb of these big, broad-leafed trees with their determination to release carefully-directed torrents of collected rain down your neck, even when precipitation from the actual heavens has eased off for half a minute.

Wetness, and the state of mind it induces in you – my dear young family caravanner – can start to feel permanent. There's the depth of this little valley; the fact that one kid's got earache, the other croup; there's no shop for miles and no bus will ever come here, or ever has; the reproachful certainty that you're out of bread and low on milk. And there's also the fact that this is Herefordshire, that this site is full-to-busting with vans and that it will clearly never stop raining until long after we have all been swept away downstream by that river, rising by the second, just the other side of the fence….

And boy, is it raining. Several roads in the area are already flooded and closed. It rained all yesterday, it rained all night and it's still raining this morning.

At 3 a.m., hearing the sound of a door slammed, you pushed aside your curtain, moving carefully so as not to wake *her*, even though you're pretty sure neither of you can really have been asleep – and you saw, splattering purposefully towards the toilet-block from the doorway of that wacky old German-built motorhome opposite, a solitary figure. He was wearing, under a wax jacket whose zip apparently doesn't work, a checked lumberjack-shirt and long khaki shorts, a dripping, straw cricket-umpire-hat and flip-flop sandals. He's that old guy who lent you his adjustable spanner last night to free off your gas-bottle and then, inviting you into a dated, dim interior, offered you a couple of tumblers of scotch. He's got a grizzled jaw and shaved-short thinning hair and seems convinced he's a loner – but still told you a load of stuff about his parents, for God's sake: what seemed like half his life-story.

You can only assume it was accidentally the uninteresting half.

Looks like he's not with anyone, just now. There was maybe a bad history somewhere… or something. Whatever it might have been. His recurring phrase: "I suppose it was for the best, really" in an educated, slightly-northern accent.

Later, this morning, you glance across to his pitch and – look – it's empty, and this rain's collecting in puddles on what was his shadow.

You've got a slight hangover. You hope he has, too.

You've just met Captain Kamper.

13th May, 2006

He's arrived at a beautiful wooded campsite in the Pay du Tarn. 'Camping Les Clots'.

It's green down the track. Trees dapple in the sunlight. The entrance is a farm gateway. To the left is a tumbledown stone hut containing a table, a chair, a logo-stickered fridge for ice-cream and a bell hanging from a beam.

He rings the bell. The woman's already on her way up the slope from the house below the entrance-track. It transpires she's Dutch. She offers to show him the site. "Our first visitor of the season". So he parks Lotte in a quiet, luminous glade and rejoins her for the tour. She apologises for the fact that two of the showers are new and still need connecting. She conscientiously reminds him to mind his head against old beams that are, in any case, twelve inches above his head (he's barely taller than his dad was) and marked with yellow-and-black tape. Her husband's up a ladder fixing some electrics.

The Captain likes these people. They're the sort of people with whom he would naturally make friends anywhere. She's making bread this morning, she says. Would he like some? Of course he would. He drove late last night and early this morning to get here, parked overnight in an *aire*. He's a bit spaced. He's also ravenous. He already knows he's going to stay here for three or four days. Come back here to Reception in an hour, she tells him, for a fresh loaf.

Back at the van, he plugs the van into the electricity supply. He takes a stroll, promising himself he'll take a proper walk later. Kuys is still up his ladder. He gets under an efficient, modern shower. The facilities are just fine. An hour after arrival, he's back at that Reception-hut, ringing the bell as requested, and Peggy is walking briskly up towards him bearing the steaming brown bread-loaf in a cloth. His towel rolled under his left arm, he waves with his right, steps forward to meet his second breakfast or early lunch, and the slick heel of his new hiking-boot slips on a worn, mossed stone.

Someone somewhere flicks a switch.

He's lost his breath and is on his back, on top of two steps and a big, square-cornered, stone plant-pot. He hasn't dropped his towel.

There's something seriously wrong. There's pain, more serious and deep-seated than he wants or needs.

She drives him 30 kilometres to the hospital in Albi.

Quickly, carefully and with good grace they check that there's no internal bleeding. Then the X-rays reveal without difficulty three broken ribs, right round at the back. Three cracked ribs? No, says the cool, efficient young woman doctor, they are *cassées*, broken, yes. (She makes a sign like breaking a baguette. Ha ha, very funny, he thinks.)

This was a bad fall, yes. Trois côtes – ribs – very painful. But Monsieur, you should be happy! A fall like this was bad, tres grave, tres fort, to break bones like this. But regardez … perhaps you could have bash your head, your skull, yes? With this force? Or breaking the back, the spine. Those are serious injuries. You have not puncture the lung! We see many Urgences from such a fall. The ribs are very painful, absoluement. But your brain, your spine and everything inside, is OK. OK? This is what is important for you.

These fractures will be very painful for a while. There is no treatment to make them better, Monsieur; they will heal in time. Here is a prescription for anti-inflammatory and painkiller. They are strong, you should not drive, OK? Have you a card for EU health-care? Oh, EHIC? Good. You will take this to the pharmacie for the drugs. Also to the office at the other part of the hospital. This way you claim back for treatment.

…Yes, Monsieur… But since I work here with Urgences, I do not like to say, "Au Revoir"!

Adieu, then, Madame. Et merci beaucoup.

So, understand, now, Captain, far from home in your house-on-wheels: it may be too late today, but let's hope not too late in your life, to realise that you need to be doing nothing more adventurous than: collecting a loaf on a clear day, when –

A bolt of lightning on an ordinary day – and look, today's actually the 13th – needs no warning clouds from which to strike. Where you had thought at last to achieve your free-striding, solo-aviating independence, you've finally achieved mortality, or at least your own first proper sense of it. Many would say you're fortunate in your delayed appreciation of that reality.

Lie down, Captain, back in your van, and sigh deeply with resignation but at least, at last, rest.

Aaaa.

But within fifteen seconds you're in agony. You *can't* lie down, on back, front or either side, without pain that gets *worse*, not better.

And now you can't get up, either! Ach, ach. Fuck. Shit. After ten minutes' struggling and weeping, you absurdly, and deliberately, roll off your bench-seat bed onto the floor.

Aaaa.

Thank goodness you first worked out the right order for doing that, legs first, in order to be half-upright against the seat and the pain.

It won't be for another ten days you'll again try anything so ambitious as horizontality – and then it'll be only to curse yourself unsparingly again for your stupidity, before repeating the same enforced, ridiculous, cursing, despairing flop.

Aaa.

He does, now, indeed, resolve to stay at least his full four days in this beautiful campsite. Peggie and Kuys leave him alone, except, kindly, to let him know he can use their phone-line and computer to email the Muse. He doesn't know how far he'll be able to drive, or even if. But Lotte has power-steering, of course. By email, and by text when he can walk far enough back up the valley to get a mobile-signal (this is after the second day), he pleads for time.

She says, he should fly home.

He explains: No no, he's vertical, he'll be OK. The weather's glorious.

(Too glorious, too hot, for the couple of hours in the afternoons when he sits and sweats and dozes and jumps with rib-twists, screams when he sneezes at the frisky May-pollen, shifts and sweats some more and tries not to weep.)

That internal sense of youth? That sense, vauntingly secret, well into middle-age and beyond, that inside him he is – eighteen – or only *slightly* older – still In His Prime, and therefore invulnerable…. Of course there's been knocks and bruises on the way, both physical and moral. There's been slings and arrows, there's been love and loss and love and children and divorce and despair and recovery and love – and work; work, always some sort of work. Always, resilience. What doesn't kill you makes you stronger. Pleased that now at last he has only himself, really, to look out for, as for herself has the Muse; and they're both tough, independent sorts …

But you know what has to be done, when your old telly isn't receiving properly, when there seems to be a fault with reception? Give it a kick! Or your laptop's frozen? Turn it off, mid-programme, and on again. In just the same way, it takes a shock, or a knock, or a second's black-out, finally to readjust your body-clock, so that you're receiving Reality properly again.

This – is that Re-boot.

He remembers a story he once read in a book on Buddhism: the irritatingly-persistent little student-Zen-monk asked the Master plaintively for the umpteenth time how he might ever attain Enlightenment. And the Master, in the end and very understandably, gave him a sharp, judicious smack on the head with a stick.

That worked…

And the Captain *is* still lucky. For some people, mortality *does* come much earlier, much too early, and much too seriously, and it's all over. As Madame the Doctor, young as she is, knows very well.

For others, maybe it will come as an illness gradually limiting their behaviour, requiring indefinite medication and care. The Captain reflects he's had a couple of minor conditions, but never believed that they might be anything other than temporary – or at least, in the medium term, best ignored.

And then, most people – for God's sake, Captain – *most people* always, at every stage of their lives, know *exactly* how old they are, and *what that means*. Don't they?

Oh, but this has come to him as a personal Attack. It's an ambush. It's like being shot in the back. Worse still, he's learnt now that he is shootable. Vulnerable not just to whims of the gods of Fortune, toward whom he may if he chooses (he's done it before) snap his fingers or flick them in a V-sign; nor to some creeping illness of which he will not otherwise think. No, he can, also, now, literally, be dashed against rocks. He is breakable.

He knows from young Madame the Doctor that this particular crisis, however painful, will not remotely be the one that carries him off. But this body, which has taken over the years plenty of football, cricket, rugby, work and gardening injuries along with a couple of minor medical "procedures" – and has always taken, it feels, mere minutes to reset itself afterwards – this body does not feel today, after the 13th of this month, nor will it feel for far too long, ready to bridge those gaps in the cells of his bones.

It'll take more time for this *second* imaginary bullet to penetrate. His nervous system, drugs or no drugs, will not be prepared to shrug off pain at any time in the first six weeks of the curative process. And he won't find that his brain can switch any more, as it always has, into assuming something simply hasn't happened – or that if it has, it can be joked or jollied away. But he's got to be OK for when the Muse flies out to join him...

And he's yet to learn that for more than three weeks, no matter where they'll be, the only way he will be able to sleep at all will be sitting up in Lotte's front passenger-seat, swivelled inwards and in part-recline, feet across on his driving-seat, on a good dose of the painkillers he's been told he can't use at all when driving. And for almost a week after the 13th – maybe it's the drugs, maybe it's the shock, or both – his digestive system seems absolutely to go on strike. It may well be that the living shit has been entirely scared out of, or frozen inside, him.

Then, on his third day at Campsite Les Clots, waking gratefully from a fevered dream of being beaten up on a piece of waste-ground by a former goalkeeper of Wolverhampton Wanderers FC, his eye is caught by a sort of movement that is not quivering grass, not shimmering leaves: inside his house on wheels, along the edge of the side-window frame, beside the left-hand-driving-seat. Along the ledge now, a black, fluid movement, like blood. But not subject to gravity, it moves both along, and upwards.

Up the edge of the window...

Ants.

They must have climbed up on a wheel, along struts, up inside the wheel-arch ... No, maybe along below the engine and thus somehow (the pedal-space, the fuse-box!?) into the cab ... Or no, up the outside, then, and through some micro-space in the fitted corner of the window? After an inspection tour, there's no sign of *where* they've come from, *outside* the van.

But they *are inside*. Little modest black ants with, unlike him, no individualistic delusions. Single-mindedly about their communal business.

They're inside, and they're walking in file. Or rather two files, one file back, the other, forth, into and out of Lotte, his house, his cave, his nest ... More of them walking in, than out. Continuous. Tens of them. Hundreds. Organized, on some chemical track. And obviously, ants don't *just* come in hundreds. Start multiplying for the ones you can't see.

Is this the painkiller-induced equivalent of *delirium tremens*? No, they're horribly real, and they aren't pink.

Even in the reduced condition in which he has found himself, the Captain's sure he's kept his van clean. He even knows, because a little light dusting and his monumental case of anal retention are his only permitted obsessions at present, that there are maybe fewer breadcrumbs, marmalade-blibs, cheese-smears around than usual. But anyway, how could even the collective-intuitive power of a French ant-colony have decided, through all that hot rubber-and-diesel stink, *from outside*, that there was something in here worth having, in his cupboards or fridge?

Even Marmite doesn't smell *that* strong.

Have they just – popped in on spec? But – there are even Vulture-ants here! – they're walking across his ceiling! They're exploring the shelves in the toilet! Maybe they're considering moving house, or at least setting up a house-share. He's been here only three days...

Stay still for too long, the undergrowth closes in. It's a scene from a low-budget horror!

He may be drugged and poorly, but there are three things he must do.

Today, now, he must drive up to the hardware store in the village and get some ant- killing stuff.

On return, he must park on a different pitch.

Tomorrow, he must check out, and leave.

Part One

The Quest, and Setting Forth

England, December 2009 – April 2010

You can check out any time you like, but you can never leave

'Hotel California' – Felder, Henley, Frey 1977

Chapter 1

A map – the Muse – the Log – the Tape – Italy, 1943 – Cyril –
& struggling out of suits –a Wedding – the daughters – the Plan – "Results"?

It's pre-Christmas, 2009. He has presents to wrap and cards to write. They're in neat heaps on the table.

So naturally instead he's spread a map across the carpet. As usual, he's in at least two places at once. Christmas list, mainland Europe – and family.

Since that "retirement" of '05, and the following year's unforgettable six-week trip taking in the Accident and Emergency Unit at Albi Hospital, the Captain has by now covered a lot of miles in trans-European camper-van trips. Father of three daughters (late teens to early thirties) of two earlier partnerships, and relict of a thirty-plus-year career in education, he's now partner of a full-time psychotherapist (hereinafter "the Muse"). And he's been relishing becoming something entirely, playfully new. In that lovely old van he's found a new self – his own picaresque protagonist: Captain of his own soul, and hero of unwritten tales which begin with the exhilaration of "setting out upon the road".

Lotte the German motorhome is parked across the street. Next to the cemetery.

It's cold outside, and he's glad to be warm.

As usual, in the front room, the Muse is working, listening to a client. Therapy. Familiar, unintelligible murmur of monologue, dialogue, silence, from down the long, dark hallway of their hundred-year-old end-terrace.

And in the living-room a map is spread on the floor like a boyhood board-game: it's Michelin's Western Europe, alongside various guidebooks and the Caravan-club book, opened face downward on the carpet, sheltering its world of secrets. All this has become usual for him at some pressure-point each winter since they got back from that very first joint expedition – always referred to as "the broken ribs trip" – five years ago. Each spring, or summer, or autumn, new adventures have to be planned across a UK or European map. He'll often set off singly, with her joining him later. And the prospect must be savoured in the planning: already they've sampled Ireland, France, Spain, Andorra, Switzerland, northern Italy, Slovenia, Croatia…

Now he's looking hard at Italy again, but more to the south – and this dark December, he has an extra book on hand to guide him.

It's serge-blue, board-backed, cloth-card-bound, in the manner of old accounts-books. Its official legend, printed black and heavy on the front cover, reads:

The Captain's own surname is handwritten in fountain-pen on this line. Of course though, it isn't in this case his own name – but his father's name and number, and in his father's handwriting, from World War II.

The "old man" died in 1984. The Captain hasn't often, over the years, consulted this operational relic. Nonetheless he does seem to have some parts of it imprinted in his head, as well as the handwriting, which in its way is still to him a living tone of voice.

Somewhere in a drawer he also has a cassette tape, the last literal record of that voice. Molecules of vocalisation, read by magnets in 1982 or 83. It opens thus:

> "In the Second World War, my military profession was that of Air Gunner (and I'm drawing my old age pension next week, and I'm still here, so That's All Right) ...

> "I don't know whether it affected many other fellows the same way, but it did strike me that, if I were to be killed at this time, I hoped it would be by enemy action. The longer the War lasted, the more this feeling hung over me that I should be very annoyed, indeed, if I got killed in some – stupid mishap or other –"

But anyway, this Log Book: less personal than the Cassette, but looked on as a historical source, much-more usefully detailed. His dad's Observer's and Air-Gunner's Flying Log Book is the actual old paperwork, the 'Bumf': the record as required by C.O. and by RAF regulation of every occasion the 'old man' took off and landed in an Air Force aeroplane. That was: between October 1941 at RAF Evanton in gunnery training, and his eventual de-mob in November 1945 – by which time he had himself, through wartime promotion, become an air gunnery instructor.

The planes he'd taken off in, in action and otherwise, had always, one way or another, returned. Fortunate that, thinks the Captain: otherwise he, his brothers and his sister wouldn't themselves have had *their* stories – let alone been able to watch offspring write their own new chapters....

In its page-format, the Log is similar to a gridded book of business-accounts, set out in columns across a double-page spread:

Date/ Hour/ Aircraft Type and No/ Pilot/ Duty/ Remarks (inc. results of bombing, gunnery, exercises etc/ Flying Times Day/Night/

And in the top corner of each right-hand page is a box for

Time Carried Forward

Dry ledger-entries. From these, however, the Captain has come to know that his father's total RAF flying hours were 292 hours and 10 minutes by Day and 14 hours 5 minutes by Night. Apparently "Hours" were scrupulously to be recorded as totals of Day and Night Flying; but not as totals of say, combat and non-combat.

Under the header "Duty": the house-style denoting a combat mission is "Ops as Briefed". Each "Ops" in the Duty cell of the logbook's account has been annotated by his dad with a little superscript number in the corner[1]. This clerical fastidiousness is what allows the old man's son to note over his coffee-mug that the first of these "Ops" was on the 18th of March 1943, flying out of Marsa Gardane to bomb the Mareth Line in Libya.

And just nine months after that particular "Tour" began, the 72nd and last of those happy landings took place at Foggia, central Italy, after attacking 'Gun positions W of San Ambrogio'. That's when they let him go back home, since those "Ops as Briefed" of the Old Man's now amounted to 176 operational hours.

Virtually the whole of the Desert Air Force war-career logged here had been riding shotgun as an air-gunner of 223 Squadron, attacking one defensive Line or another, first in support of Montgomery's Eighth Army through North Africa, then over the Med, through Sicily and up through Italy – as far as to the Volturno Line, and then the Barbara, and the Bernhardt, and the Gustav Lines – and almost all of this was in broad daylight – in American-built twin-engined Baltimore "light bombers", each crewed by four airmen: a pilot, a navigator/bomb-aimer, a wireless operator and an observer/gunner. All this Action took place in 1943.

The Father:

---

[1] Like this

The Captain, even into his fifties, has more-or-less consciously lived in attempted rebellion from this man, whom nonetheless he's always deeply respected and loved.... Let's say his father's the centre of a set of knots from which, like so many men, he's still trying to unbind. The Captain imagines pushing himself free from something like a tangle of serpents – Laocoon-like, but he hopes eventually with more success. He remembers his dad divesting himself of an overall in the back of his ironmonger's shop in just such a way at the end of his working day.

Now again he imagines him before he was *anyone's* father struggling out of a bulky RAF flying-suit and parachute harness.

And now he imagines himself, wriggling out of something heavy: shrugging away, shedding, an older, outer skin: often protective, always constricting.

Like the shreds of a dream, above all he feels he won't ever quite shake off his own old suit of Duty: work, paternity, enforced reliability. He's almost sixty. It wasn't such a plague when he was young. Now he looks back on his life and sometimes sees one, with all its obvious differences, too much like the old man's. Of course there are genes: who knows how deep *they* go? And there's also the parental model... Nature and nurture...

Dad. Long gone. 1984... twenty-six years now. Such a good man ... but this was a dad he never in his adult years consciously *wanted* to copy. The frustrated commercial-artist. The dapper young chap with the raffish tash. The wartime air-gunner. The widower. The weary moralist. The husband twice over. The man of compromise and consideration. The ironmonger in the brown overall shop-coat. The debating-society's liberal spokesman. The smart, grave, grey-haired school-governor. The voice on the tape...

... and the poor, quiet, reedy man with the piss-hole-in-the-snow-eyes who too soon would be waiting in the "convalescent" hospital alongside a man with no legs, to be allowed to die in his sixties of chronic kidney-failure. The patient, yes: patient, pale, resigned; only faintly-resentful.

Not the way to go. How many different suits had he worn, the old man?

But he was trying to get out of that damned horrible war-flying-suit right to the end. The cassette-tape had meant he needed at last to tell people something. Yes, the old man does need to go back, and if not dropped, at last perhaps be cured.

1960s. A boy's Airfix kits. The thing is, nobody *else* had asked the questions. But had *he* asked them for the right reasons?

This Christmas, though, there's a new "coincidence". Aha. Oh yes. Lighten up!

The Captain's middle daughter, social worker Laura, late twenties, is planning to enact her wedding, next May, in romantic Sorrento ... Yes, OK, even if we *are* now, in late 2009, living in a post-Crash world.... He winces. But next year, defiantly, they're going, she and Ian, to beautiful Sorrento on the magnificent Amalfi Coast, to be married in the opulent open air by the town's Registrar. It was her elder sister Emma (just left Lehmann Brothers!) who gave her the idea. She'll be a bridesmaid. So will youngest sister, Freya.

He can completely understand their vision of this event, even though his own *two* weddings (so long ago now, it seems, and neither of them to the Muse ...) were much more in the fashion of their '70s and '80s days: low-key, almost postmodern registry-office events in Oldham and Rochdale. So certainly, he can be a little puzzled by this decision of Laura's. At the same time he must admire and wonder at her off-sprung determination to live in her own way and to match her own times. He's talked it through with her, and with Ian and his parents. A budget including his own contribution, has been agreed. The plan's been set in motion.

Hmm. And thus...

A sort of serendipitous opportunity... for him... to combine two trips.... Create some circularity ... Fathers. A simultaneous tying of new, and untying of old, knots. Join harmoniously in the optimistic world of 21st century young lovers. Let go – give away! – some parental responsibilities.

And first, on the way there, load up old Lotte, and take old Dad – or at least his book and his cassette tape – back out of this here-and-now and into his Past – into Battlefield Italy.

The country he helped to bomb to bits in 1943.

But let's face it, he and his pals weren't expected to hold any reckoning of what might be happening thousands of feet below, when the high-explosives landed – except, with proper pride in achievement, noting on a number of occasions,

"Bombing Results Good".

There was no such phrase back then as "Collateral Damage". The word was: Duty.

In one of his later books, John Steinbeck wrote of his own war-experience:

> … Men in prolonged battle are not normal men. And when afterwards they seem to be reticent – perhaps they don't remember very well.[2]

The Day, Laura's wedding date, has been set: 18th May, 2010. Just hope it doesn't rain. Rain? In May in Sorrento? Don't be silly. Anyway, joyously, he'll need to be there, on that day, and ready to "give her away"… So that's the date, the marker to plan towards and around. Now *that's* decided, so much else begins to fit! He remembers that one prospective bridesmaid, Laura's youngest sister Freya, said only a few months ago that she'd definitely fancy another van-trip, after her A Levels …

And their friends, Tina and Bill, live in Tuscany … So he could meet up with *the Muse* there, after the wedding, and then she and he can do some extra touring afterwards. (She doesn't need, or want, to be on the necessarily-restricted wedding-guest list: "Your girls have got enough mothers".)

This plan of his to pursue his Dad's places in Italy was already cooking, somewhere, before. On a back burner. But now, Laura's unwittingly made it happen! You see, if you're open to the world, he murmurs complacently, life composes itself around you!

---

[2] 'Once there was a War', 1943, 1958. Reprinted Folio Society 2013. (Thanks to Freya for finding it.)

Christmas soon … Ho ho bloody ho. Back to the guide-books. He opens his Michelin Italy Road Atlas at the Index pages, and starts to pull out all the Log's named airfields and "targets" laboriously from the index, onto file-cards; then to number those targets, by the order of his father's bombing operations, onto the maps.

How long would it take to visit all of these places properly? Obviously much, much too long for *all*. But with a bit of extra research, a fair selection can be made.

Again though, a phrase repeats between his ears:

"Bombing Results …."

Good?

Chapter 2

The 'Off '– van & aeroplane – usefulness of the older man? – 1938-9 –
stepping down...

Fifty-eight-year-old Captain Kamper – child of the Fifties, Sixties teenager –
is up on a high field by a farmhouse in the hills above Whitby. If you were to
drive by (and it's unlikely you would, this April Sunday morning, unless you
lived locally) you might at first glance suppose that the farmer is developing
a sideline, selling dairy ice-cream: the Captain's motor-home is roughly the
size of that sort of van, and she *is* cream in colour. In some lights in fact
Lotte looks very much like a gigantic Nineties freezer with windows.

Here he is, waking at 4 a.m., out of a confused dream, under familiar
pressure from his bladder. He'll still be struggling three quarters of an hour
later, desperate to switch off again and sleep.

In the darkness, or pale dawning, of trying to get back to sleep, there's
nothing to block the view. Pre-dawn anxieties, discomforts, must-be-dones
and wish-I-hadn'ts, and shreds of discreditable dream. Weird patterns
behind his eyelids, part of him…. That imaginary draught at his waistband.
Soon enough, a funny little worrying pain. And how is it going to be, what's
to be done, when he *has* got up…?

He's keyed by the excitement, and already starting to be pursued by the
guilt, of being away from home again: on his own, ready to fly. Of what he is
leaving behind. Of who…

But today is the day. So he may as well get up, as lie here and stew.

And now he's off his bed, out of his sleeping-bag. But the propane-and-
coffee-scented interior's warm and he's looking out over the lid of his cooker

with a smile at the red-tiled roofs of North Yorkshire sandstone farm-buildings, here and in the middle-distance. He likes the shape of the black-limbed trees (it's early spring-time) against the blue of the sky. He likes the way that the place is quiet and still, apart from the breath of the heating kettle; and how even so, he can sometimes hear a breeze and feel it move the Hymer faintly on its suspension.

Far in the distance, even the sea's visible, just over a hedge it seems; but five miles away. An occasional middle-distance shotgun report can be heard, and a wheeling squall of rooks he can't see.

The rolling green field twinkles like a cloud. Oddly, in this heavy motor, her big rough tyres sunk half-an-inch in brown, glistening ruts, he feels that he's not really on land at all. Not "parked up". No, but instead, that he's flying. Floating. Hovering: above a coast, a town, a hillside, the world. And not in an old German campervan – maybe an aeroplane?

He's close to home here and yet also Captain of the ether, of wide fresh air – of all he surveys, from coffee-mug to cloud. He knows his particular enjoyment of the adventure of vanning is no different in many ways from other campers'. Still, he does know his take on it is also peculiar, irrational; his own strange dream entirely.

Now he's a free agent, he's been able to spend some of his own money, sometimes with a clear conscience, on himself. Five years ago, after the moment of revelation from that last-minute lorry-driver, he put that chunk of his retirement lump-sum into buying this twelve year-old Hymer, and added in the four-and-a-half grand from his Mum's Will into a theoretical ("this'll cover the depreciation for a while. Thanks, Mum – you always liked your caravan holidays at Reighton") Fund.

He does have a house, of course – or at least the Building Society (now a "Bank") has a house – and therefore he still has a bit of a mortgage, thanks to the settlements he's made to his former partners (not, he reminds himself sternly, because of any fault on his part, but just in order to be clear of any possible further claim). Anyway: maybe they should just sell their big house now, he and The Muse. They could easily move into something smaller... Maybe even into Lotte... But no, the kids like to come and visit, and some concessions have to be made to their desire (in contrast to his feelings at their age) for some measure of paternal conventionality ...

So what he's doing here is: he's *experimenting* with life in the van. He'd *like* to be in it and away all the time. Partly, like a sullen small child he really can't see why he can't: "Why *can't* I?" But in the end he doesn't want to become too completely the apprentice hermit and signed-up Sad Git he knows he easily could.

After thirty-odd years teaching the country's new generations, he's learning he no longer retains any enthusiasm any more for struggling with the unreasonableness of others – which Doing Good (in the world) always entails. He's got enough on his plate now, just dealing with *his own* unreasonableness. But it is a puzzle and a struggle. His molecules are still, now as always, pointing the wrong way, or every-which-way. Maybe the huge. distant magnets of world and national events have deranged his wiring.

He did always want to Do Good. If he could. Back then.

Now he just wants to be frugal. And wise. Fat chance... So why is he choosing to keep up a house and (instead of living in that) blundering around in a gas-guzzling house on wheels? It's a puzzle to him, and will lead to many more. Such as:

Anyway – actually – what is the *use* of the Older Man?

This morning – early-waking to head south, on the first, local, English stage of his expedition – he still holds, while rising and starting the kettle, a fragment of dream.

In which he descended from his van, as if from an old plane onto an airfield.

And in fact, in the real world, his rectangular, round-cornered motor-caravan door – the doorway he stands in now, cradling his coffee – does actually open from Lotte's fuselage in the *middle* of one side, and two feet above the ground. It's his only door, and it's much the same shape, opens in much the same way, as the door of an old passenger-aircraft (say, Neville Chamberlain's, back from Munich, in those 1938 newsreels from just before his father's war). A little clanky step gets released below it by operation of an interior lever, and from this he can step easily down onto *terra firma*.

Prime Minister Chamberlain might indeed have felt a bit the same touching back down at Heston Aerodrome in 1938. So too a German tank-commander, jumping down just a little later over the Polish border…. Or Hitler, from his triple-engined Junkers or his later Condor.

Or himself in the dreams of his youth, stepping down from Dan Dare's spaceship onto another planet. Or later from Neil Armstrong's, onto the moon.

Cor. Trippy stuff this camper-vanning. Thing is, once you start to open a worm-hole into the past…

Chapter 3

On the road – Bookworlds – Etna, Empedocles, Arnold – oh sorry, Lotte –

Chocks away …

Over onto the A1.

Leeds.

M1 South.

South.

And across. West now.

It starts to rain. Always does over here, for him. Herefordshire that time... God. This time he's booked-in, in advance, to a site near Hay-on-Wye. Why wouldn't he like the place? The Bookshop-bubble. He can stock up his road-rolling cupboard-shelves with an extra few second-hand treasures. From New Year's researches he's made a hopeful list: Morandi, Pirandello...

Already packed his Steinbecks, Milligan, Newby. And one more, even quirkier choice: "The Tape" mainly tells that one time, flying north from an airfield in Sicily, his Dad had a very close brush with Mount Etna... And legend has it, the celebrated Ancient Greek poet and philosopher Empedocles, who first formulated the classical idea of the Four Elements, Earth, Air, Water and Fire, actually threw himself out of his life down into the maw of that very volcano. Victorian poet and critic Matthew Arnold wrote a play and a poem about "Empedocles on Etna".

Volcanoes are certainly becoming a theme. Sorrento's only just across the Bay from Vesuvius. Only yesterday, his last day before leaving, he vaguely heard news of a volcano erupting in Iceland. Already, today, it's disrupting airline flights up in northern Europe. And there's a bigger one, said to be priming itself now to blow right alongside it. They say that the last time *that one* blew, it was very big deal indeed....

Anyway he's chucked in Empedocles (though today all that's left of him is a few hundred fragmentary lines of verse and a much bigger bunch of notes from scholars through the ages) – and Matthew Arnold for luck.

And at Hay, he hopes he'll find again that Norman Lewis "Naples" book. Sorrento, Naples, Vesuvius.... Read it a few years back, then must have lent it to someone – but who?

Oh and... yes. Sorry. You're maybe a motorhome enthusiast, and that's the only reason you picked up this book?

What about Lotte, you say?

Well, Lotte the Hymermobil 550S is a heavy, German cargo-bearing chassis and a five-cylinder diesel truck motor; a sheet-metal, coach-built container under a cream plasticised coating. '550' means: five and a half metres long. Left-hand drive. Automatic transmission. Built: 1992. One previous owner, German, female, say the documents. To the Captain back in '05 this purchase was personal and idiosyncratic, an impatient lurch to buy an old camper-van he immediately liked the feel of. But those who, unlike him, are really *interested* in trucks, vans, and classic marques of motor-home, keep telling him: she's Special. S means: Special. He already knows this, but in an intimate, personal way. As soon as, without stooping, he first set foot inside her in the dealer's yard, she'd absorbed herself into his head, and become unquestionably an extension of his interior, as he of hers.

"The last one they made properly", they say, the *cognoscenti*. And like the Tardis, like the Captain himself, Lotte makes sense only from the inside. There's only that one door, and you couldn't get a camel through it. You step in from the right-hand side (in Greater Europe, obviously, this is the pavement-side). Your right hand rests on the velour top of the swivelling passenger's seat, behind the deep, curved dashboard and a high, deep wraparound windscreen. You glance down and across to where you'll sit, the Captain's chair behind a big, black, bus-driver's steering-wheel. Over this cab-space, a false-ceiling effect: but this is a double bed – it can be released and lowered to chest-height on smooth hinges. A hooked ladder rests on the bedding. Generally this is the guest bed, and can be curtained off. Two of his daughters shared it on the Costa Brava.

Still at the door, your left hand rests on the reinforced glass of the gas-hob's lid. Directly ahead of you, in expensive undertaker's cherry-wood veneer, gleams the door to a toilet and wet-room; opening this door reveals a skylight over a two-and-a-half feet square cubicle of off-cream plastic – basin, bog, shelves, hooks, shower-head, drain – everything fitted to the millimetre. Close it. Next left, a wardrobe-cupboard, over a rumbling propane heater. Early-90s velour upholstery stretches round the rear, clockwise left, in a seven-foot-by-seven-foot inverted u-shape lounge-banquette, faded grey-mauve in pattern, between whose sides stands a table with a streaked ersatz-marble-effect top, cherry-rimmed, on heavy, crossed ironing-board legs. This table can be lowered, too, so that the cushions of the bench seats, slid together on top of it from the side benches and across the centre-back of the van, can create another, more-than-double, bed. Above the seating, and the windows, sides and back, now see: a marvellous row of twelve high, fitted cupboards. To him, this recalls Steinbeck's Rocinante, whose interior had been custom-built for the yacht-loving Nobel Laureate "like a ship's cabin".

Finally, the kitchen-sink over a fitted cupboard for kettle and pans; and right next to you at the door, under your left hand, that gas-hob-top, over the fridge. On the floor: cream vinyl with a grey fleck. The ceiling: curved, curiously fluffy, a stab at noticeable insulation. Every fitting, hinge, catch and switch: neat, functional, efficient, exact.

So. Lotte Is Beautiful: unfashionably well-made, a hymn to enclosed integration, a heavily-defended womb on wheels. German-built, a five-cylinder Mercedes diesel engine in front; and behind the driver everything as solid and precise as the machinery under the hood.

At home, or in winter storage, poor Lotte will sit and wait – with two yellow hi-viz jackets draped over her front seats – cold and damp, will wait for months. Then at last, when he gets in, sits in his Captain's adjustable high-backed seat and turns the key, she'll start. First time, and exactly as if the last time was an hour ago. As if to rebuke him! "Where have you been?" She's a vehicle, she's transport, she's supposed to be moving, taking him somewhere. She's not Robert Louis Stevenson's quirky, unwilling Modestine. Her engine is sewing-machine-crisp, she's loyal and true. She's supposed to be moving, today and tomorrow, and was therefore always supposed to have been moving yesterday.

On the streets of their home city, thrumming patiently at say, a pedestrian crossing: people's eyes widen, they even tend to gawp. It's bogglement, at her rare and dated lines, mixed with envy at the blob of eccentric freedom she must always represent to a gaze that rests on her in the middle of a working day. He sometimes even tries to feel bad about that.

On the broad highway, other Vanners wave and smile. Now *there's* a van, they say.

Why is it that ships are always referred to as She, even when the name's Dreadnought? Easy, we know: because the old sailors were always lonely – or at any rate, because they wanted to project their feelings onto something as consistent and caring as they wished their mothers, wives or mistresses had been. So anything that gets a man there and brings him back home again tends to be personified optimistically in the feminine.

Dad, he thinks, I bet your wartime pilot, Flight Sergeant (later Warrant Officer) Bob Connell, didn't feel any different. I'll bet he called Martin Baltimore IIIA, P Peter, No. 342 of 223 Squadron, "she". I bet you all did.

"The old crate's done us a favour again today, hasn't she?"

Though they've travelled far in their time together and will continue to share many an adventure or narrow squeak, the Captain does know that this van at the same time *is just a van* … Even so, there can be times, say when at the top of a Pyrenean pass he's not sure whether to halloo at the beauty or to weep with relief…. if there's no-one beside him in the navigator's seat to reach out a hand to…. There's always Lotte herself to be patted lovingly upon the steering column and be told "Thank you again, you beautiful beast" – or something equally emphatic, meaningless and (in any other circumstance) embarrassing.

And she's always, however reluctantly, had a personality. Ever since his dear old Mum, nearly sixty years ago, read him picture story-books about Noddy And His Little Car, it's been obvious to the Captain that all motor vehicles have their facial expressions: headlamps for eyes, radiator-grill noses, bumper mouths. Sometimes Lotte can look, particularly if parked with her offside front wheel turned out, as if she's wisecracking drily from the corner of heavy lips. And *if* she spoke, what would she say?

You can give her a bit of a Marlene Dietrich accent if you like. "What's up, wise guy? Maybe I'm not beautiful any more, but I'm prepared to go to the ends of the earth with you. Meanwhile" – bitter sigh – "I'll just wait here, and try to look like your house."

She has beautiful square eyes.

Chapter 4

Ageing – stupid mishaps – Churchill – retirement – Cyril 1916-39

One thing the Captain (in common with many of his generation) still can't get his head around, is ageing. Couple of weeks back, at home, in one of the Muse's psychological journals, he found an article on the difficulties and struggles of "Men in Mid-Life". He read it with considerable interest, recognising issues in his own life, traits of himself as he did so – and then was forced to cast it aside in horror. On this topic the author concerned himself, he said, with men from thirty-five up to their early fifties.

"Shit", said the Captain. "I'm just coming to terms with the idea that I'm no longer young. Now you tell me I'm no longer middle-aged?"

He laughs incredulously at this, shaking his head – as he does as he tells his friends. Then he feels creeping upon him that other huge, unspoken dread. Until Albi Hospital, the Captain always complacently expected to live forever. Now he suspects that he always will… expect… to…. Until he doesn't. Careful on those steps now.

That's probably one reason why this Log Book, that tape, his Dad –

"I don't know whether it affected many other fellows the same way, but it did strike me that, if I were to be killed at this time, I hoped it would be by enemy action. The longer the War lasted, the more this feeling hung over me that I should be very annoyed, indeed, if I got killed in some – stupid mishap or other" – and St Peter…."

those old faces and sayings, have been starting to loom again?

Winston Churchill had a phrase to make a purpose out of the advance of years. "Keep Buggering On". And so he did in the 1950s, leading his party and his country into his own eighties. No historian now (not even, perhaps, Winnie himself as historian) would regard *those* as his Finest Hours. Some might say – Anthony Eden certainly would have said – that the Old Man in this period of his life might have better concentrated on improving his bricklaying and oil-painting techniques at Chartwell. However, Winston saw no reason to stop being Churchill, World Statesman, and one can understand that *would* be hard to give up. So he Kept Buggering On at the same things for just as long as he could.

The Captain – as many of us do – knows plenty of people who, un-Churchillian in everything except pigheadedness, take retirement in their mid-to-late fifties and seemingly stop even buggering on – and even before the years tell them they're old. Particularly men who've never had much identification with domesticity. As if they're incapable, he thinks, of seeing things differently from their own father's generation; can therefore only see the retirement-clock as a stopwatch counting-down to the coffin – ignoring the stark fact that their own fathers worked ten or more years longer than them, even before winding up that new carriage-clock on what was a much shorter life-expectancy.

Equally likely, the old dad would have dropped dead at the workface. The Captain's own father, born in 1916, drew only three years of his old-age pension.

His dad. Cyril. Had got his education all the way to age 15, a triumph for Cyril's parents who in their day hadn't even been able to progress that far. The previous generation, Cyril's grandparents, had taken *their* son Tom away from the coalfields of County Durham in the 1880s because they vowed they would never, never let him, like a good few before him, die young of a life down the pit. Better apprentice him as a baker, at arm's length in North Yorkshire. That this protective provision might culminate a couple of generations later in the Captain and his brothers – Going To University! – what puffing of pride might disturb the dust of old family urns....

Dragged away then from the coal-heap, Grandad Tom had got set up in a shop, first bakery then ironmongery.

In *his* turn, once Tom's son Cyril (born 1916) got the Municipal Schooling into him, away he was put – for a reason – in those go-getting, colourful, modern 1930s – into Gentlemen's Outfitting – away Down South, to Jaeger's, in Oxford. In that smart new world Cyril would soon learn to become knowledgeably "dapper", even modestly-dashing in appearance, as might befit the up-market sales-talker on the shop-floor.

At the same time he always had to remember: he was only a generation-step from the pit his dad had escaped, and from the rural peasants of his mother's line. While he certainly had one heck of an eye, this later-to-be-Dad of the Captain's, for fashion, sketching and the ladies – and while he shared a then-fashionable escapist taste for the facetious works of Dornford Yates – he was also anchored to an inescapable back-story: the hard-headed, ramrod-spined Methodist Church that had been his parents' meeting-place: the rock of the Chapel. So: Monday to Saturday – sports, clothes, gentlemen's suitings, ties, snappy hats. See and be seen, yes; sketch; maybe flirt – this was the world of the Thirties and these were its modern skills and pleasures. But the Old Folks would have trusted he must also know: true substance lies also in obligation, in duty and in doing right – righteously by those who have given you this promise of better things, this step upward, this road forward. Sunday-best behaviour.

Then a woman of his own town, and five years older than he – they'd met when he was a senior Scout and she a Guide-leader – continued to admire him on his visits home. They went hiking together, he bright in his plus-fours, she modern too in her slacks, up on the Moors, through the countryside of his mother's folks – and one thing may have led to another, even if all it led to at first was Talk.

His parents, perhaps because of Talk – bred of that age-difference (much more evident in a close community and in those days thought to be rather embarrassing) – couldn't, at the start, have approved. They knew what "common" meant to them. Yes, of course they knew it when they saw it: that's what they were *themselves*, underneath – what they'd always striven to clamber so cleverly away from. After all their efforts, their only lad must never be seen as *that*. That's partly why they'd sent him to stay with some of their Methodist connections down in the South – and thus had helped to get him started on a that very respectable, even stylish job. Which surely brought Prospects unlikely to be matched by a too-early marriage!

In that spell of separation, perhaps young Cyril was forced to try and see it their way too, for a while. But he'd also seen the love of his life...

And thus in 1939, as War was declared, he was 23, she 28 years old. He got Jaeger's to give him a move up to York, came back near enough to home, and in April he and Muriel were married.

Mind you, as it happened, in 1939, if you were male, 23 and *un*married, you would've got "called up" into the Forces first, *before* the married fellers...

Maybe even his parents saw a point in that.

Chapter 5

Weather cleared up last night. Not a cloud in sight now. But at the motorway service-station, waiting for his credit card to be recognised by the machine, the Captain says to the lad, "Funny light out there. Thunder on the way?"

"No", says the young man, handing him back his receipt and card. "I noticed it this morning, been weird all day. Must be the ash-cloud thing".

Ash cloud? Oh... Yes, that must be it. Unpronounceable eruption in Iceland. Ash-cloud? From Iceland? Here? Wow. Bit apocalyptic ... Wasn't it Santorini, in the Aegean, blowing its top that started the Ice Age?[1]

Ach, we know Iceland's always full of volcanic activity. One the great Icelandic sagas, Ragnarok, pictures the end of the world in a great battle of the gods and giants: all smoke, belching fires....

Oh, heck – but hang on, it does say again, on the service-station telly – good timing, this fuel-and-coffee-stop; he stays to watch – that in Iceland, they say this ash-cloud is caused by the mere little sister of a *major* volcano, Katla – and that Katla normally goes pop at about the same time... An eruption of Big Sister Katla in 1755 killed about a quarter of Iceland's population, put Europe into solid twilight and wrecked harvests for quite a while. This led some wise men at the time to speculate that the mouth of Hell itself must be in Iceland. Wo-ho – *and* 1755 was also the year of the Lisbon earthquake, so it's thought those two literally earth-shaking events were geologically linked! Not only so recently, either.

---

[1]   No, actually. But very large eruptions can affect sunlight and therefore reduce temperatures. Conversely they can add a little, over time, to the largely manmade greenhouse effect.

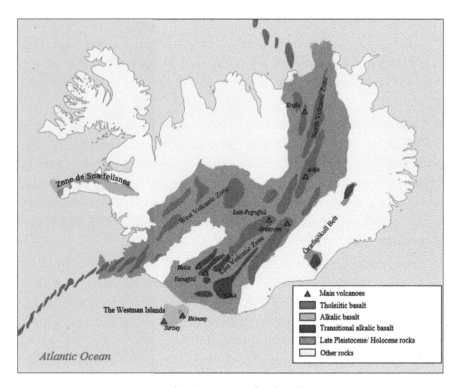

Volcanic system of Iceland[2]

Prehistoric ash-layers of several inches found right across the geology of the North, including in Scotland, are generally put down to an even earlier big bang of Katla's. So a likely new eruption of the beast (about which the Icelandic prime minister is soon heard making dry jokes on Lotte's radio) might well put Our Little Unpronounceable Kid in his place, and the rest of us back in the dark.... And for how long?

Bad earthquake in *Italy*, last year, actually – Aquila... close to his route.

Icelanders (it's their national characteristic as well as their circumstance) have no choice but to ignore these threats. On their remote land, they simply expect to deal with the consequences. They've been grimly grinning and doing so since time began. We relative southerners do the ignoring part, too – though not right now without a sort of underlying consumerist panic, he thinks. Now it's leading all the airlines, one at a time, to suspend flights

2   by Volcanic_system_of_Iceland-Map-fr.svg: Pinpinderivative work: Chris.urs-o (talk) – Volcanic_system_of_Iceland-Map-fr.svg. Licensed under CC BY-SA 3.0 via Commons – https://commons.wikimedia.org/wiki/File:Volcanic_system_of_Iceland-Map-en.svg#/media/File:Volcanic_system_of_Iceland-Map-en.svg

anywhere near the broad ash-plume which is drifting across their paths. Of course, they have their eye as much on eye-watering liability-insurance claims as on actual dangers. Diagrams start to appear, on telly, of what happens to the workings of a jet engine that ingests this pumice-dust... Not good.

Meanwhile myths of darkness and catastrophe do feel bred in the bone. Even as an adult – if he thinks about them hard, thinks about what they have done in Earth's human and climatic history – volcanoes can stir up images of his own very earliest idea of Apocalypse. In his mind's eye the Captain is seeing a plate from "The World of the Children"[3], which he probably looked at with his big sister Ros, round about 1958; or could it have been in a magazine? The "bodies" of Pompeii.

Seven years old he'd have been, he thinks. Surely a very early age to experience "the macabre" – and what's more, that "the macabre" could be actual photographic fact. That Earth-shattering, life-petrifying events really can occur at any moment, can literally burst from the ground beneath your feet. Reading that childhood picture in his head again, now ... It was the 1950s after all, and not long after, it would be explained to him – who by? – that even *worse* might occur: say, if a bald-headed, bespectacled scientist in a white coat managed to cut the smallest possible item in the world in two. (The child back then imagined a very sharp chisel – like the one the joiner cut himself with while working on putting up a new kitchen cupboard for his mum. They called it a cold chisel – and, astonishingly, that implement on its own could reduce a big strong man up a stepladder to a shivering ghost with three tightly-knotted tea-towels failing to stop a maroon flood staining the lino, as he held the door for them, and the man's mate helped the bloke out, and Mum came back from next door, after phoning the ambulance.)

Yes, so scientists cutting the absolute *tiniest* thing would apparently cause a terrible *huge* thing, with a cloud on it like an eruption. It was also the case that at any time his mum might get upset and angry and shout at his dad. This was a horror too, and he might have to run in and beg them to stop it. Where might it all end? He was a little boy who was learning he had a lot he should be anxious about.

And yes – and then he had *dreamed*, aged maybe eight, a nightmare vision about a Burst Of Flame ... He won't think of *that* again – not just now.

---

[3]   The World of the Children (Four volume set) by Stuart Miall. Caxton Publishing Co. 1955

As one grows up, real catastrophe tends to be much smaller-scale, more personal. Thirty years later, in 1986, the nucleus of his own marriage had been split. The extent of his global fears at that time can't now be defined, but M.A.D. was still very much in the air, the Cold War still "on". So in his mind, when that Threat – whatever It might be – would come, he knew, as the Single Parent Upon Whom All Depended, he would cram those two little girls of his into the back of the car and hurtle Northwards as far and as fast as he could make it. They would stick to the minor roads (because the major ones would be jammed) but they would need to make it as far as possible from major conurbations, because those would of course be targeted first …

He wasn't in a very good state in all kinds of ways back then, come to think of it.

More recently, after Reagan's Star Wars and the crumbling of the Wall, everyone was encouraged to think that the nuclear, and therefore the Apocalyptic, threat was gone; but Then: Doom had leapt back into the air again! Obviously the world's subconscious really *needs* those four horsemen and the Dance of Death, the spectre with the scythe's silhouette along the horizon. Global warming was starting to be a Thing; The "Lord of the Rings" film trilogy climaxed inside a volcano, where the Ring's sickening, radioactive evil made molecular mincemeat not just of the horrid Gollum but also the pale continuing spirit of pilgrim Frodo; meanwhile Saddam Hussein, you'll remember, didn't just have drainpipes, but Weapons Of Mass Destruction.

Then one day at work he walked into the Office, where Dave the bursar, who liked a lugubrious joke with him when time was slack, said very straight-faced: "Have you heard?"

"What, Dave?"

"A plane's flown into a skyscraper in New York."

"Oh yeah?" There's some kind of obvious joke about Americans coming up....

"No, I mean really. *Really*, Richard. It's just happened."

A newscast film scene, in which two major elements of materialist heaven, jet plane and skyscraper, were (repeatedly) being brought together to create a wormhole in reality, a fissure in the fabric.

So by the time of the 2008 economic Crash, disaster was just part of the zeitgeist, always likely tomorrow's news: his first daughter Emma started a "Post-Apocalyptic Book Club" among her post-Modern, post-Lehman, friends in London. First title on the list: Cormac McCarthy's 2006 blockbuster, "The Road" – cannibalism and all..

And now we're in 2010, and it's back to volcanoes again.

But he's making the best of it now, the Captain, as he splurts down the M40 munching a comforting petrol-station pasty. At the moment, behind the wheel, controlling what he can and must, he has no-one but himself (and other road-users) to worry about, and that's all for the best.

He's well-washed-and-scrubbed-up, but it wouldn't matter too much if he weren't. He's lowish on propane, but no-one else is worrying about it, or reminding him. If it were to run out while he cooked his tea, he'd have only himself to blame, and would certainly curse freely. Then he'd go off and sort it out. That clunk – going over the speed-bumps out of the River Wye site this morning – might well be a dodgy nearside shocker... But no-one else heard it and he'll get it fixed only when the opportunity is well in his face, and when the noise has continued long enough to irritate him. He doesn't have to bother that it's bothering anyone one else. It isn't.

This weather – warmish, but not apocalyptic. That pasty went fast. No breakfast, you see. He should make it near Portsmouth today, though. Maybe find a lorry-park somewhere near. Slide up between a couple of HGVs. A tin of soup's in the cupboard for tonight. Plenty of coffee for the morning. By that time, it'll be sea air he's tasting. Yes, he's making the best of the day, and Lotte the Hymermobil's rolling for the south coast.

He knows that Portsmouth means the ferry. The ferry means: two days to Bilbao. And soon, the south of France. And then – he'll be in Italy…

Chapter 6

October 1941 – March 1943

Cromarty – Kenya – Blenheims – Egypt – Baltimores – a skipper, a crew –
& a War

Cyril was eventually "called up" by the RAF in October 1941 and sent far
north, to Evanton on the Firth of Cromarty, No.8 Gunnery School (No.50
Course), where ten weeks later his Log got stamped and noted with: "Above
average. Should make a good air-gunner with more experience".

Turn the Log-book page, and it's nearly a year later. Cyril has arrived at 70
OTU (Overseas Training Unit), Nakuru, northwest of Nairobi. Dramatically,
shipped abroad[1], it must be at first a real facer to find himself in company
liberally sprinkled with "colonials" – South African, Canadian, Australian
and others, as well as British – training together, here in Kenya, on rapidly-
outdated Bristol Blenheim bombers. Cyril and two pals are photographed by
one another in a bright, dusty street in town, in turn grinning and holding a
huge bunch of bananas, which has cost him one shilling.

Now they shift to a final training base in Egypt. At some point Cyril is
photographed touristically – the largest photograph in the war albums – with
ten companions, on horse-and-camel-back, in front of the Great Pyramid.
He's stationed here for just two months, during which Montomery's Eighth
Army turns the tide of the war in North African, at El Alamein.

---

[1] He contracted hepatitis on the troopship. This left a weakness that probably contributed
     to his hospitalisation twice later during the war, and rather likely his death aged 68, of
     kidney failure, in 1984.

By now they're learning to operate a new, American-built plane, the modern, twin-propellered Martin Baltimore. A couple of scrupulously-accounted Log-pages further on, Cyril is introduced to the three men he'll fly with for the next year.

In Bob's later account[2], each pilot was told to choose his crew. Imagine the scene, out on the airfield – alarmingly like picking teams, old-style, for Games at school ... and here, Flt Sgt Bob Connell conducts himself rather quirkily, yet in a democratic spirit.

On the first round, Bob chooses Cliff (a fellow-Australian – "and a pretty good slow bowler") to be his wireless operator. Next, he invites his new W/Op to choose their gunner/observer, on the grounds that in an aircraft so narrow and cramped, the crew of four are effectively two separated pairs, so the gunner will be Cliff's "oppo". Thereupon Cliff, for whatever reason – maybe cricket again – picks Cyril: maybe he's demonstrated he's a keen opening bat. The three of them finally put their heads together: to select Jack as their navigator/bomb-aimer. They've seen him stand there looking rather aloof and alone, and feel they should be the ones to include him in their gang.

Now at last, January 1943, the fledgling crew – Bob Connell (Australian, pilot), Jack Glover (British, navigator/bomb-aimer), Cliff Wooster (Australian, wireless operator) with Cyril (English, air-gunner/observer) – are joined up for the first time with an actual Squadron: No. 223, RAF Desert Air Force, stationed at Landing Ground (LG) 86, Amiriya, Egypt.

There follows a stint of seven weeks' serious operational training for the unit's new boys. They fly practice formations and sorties, over Wadi Natruh, Alamein and Siwa, until the end of February, when they're given a couple of weeks' leave in Cairo and Alex.

Then, on the 18th of March, 1943, their real War starts:

Ops1 as briefed   Mareth   Accurate heavy a/a[3] over target. 1hr 40
                                No losses. No E/A[4] seen.

---

[2]   I'm eternally grateful to the late Geoff Connell and family for this recollection of his father's.

[3]   a/a = anti-aircraft fire

[4]   EA = Enemy Aircraft

Chapter 7

1960s to 1980s – "The Good Life?" –

At the end of the campsite, in a cruelly-small enclosure, lifesize, stands a plastic horse. It's realistic in every detail, except for movement and life. This is also the first campsite the Captain can remember (perhaps there have been others) where they play piped radio in the toilets: "Music Radio of the 60s, 70s and 80s!" boasts the announcer briefly between a little-known Barry White number and that irritating little song about '…San Francisco Bay … Don't Marry Her …'

The Captain comes from a generation which has much to be grateful for, and which has produced a great deal, like that musak, that it can't be proud of.

In the intervening decades since Steinbeck took his poodle for a ride ("Travels with Charley", 1960), the consumption of petroleum, and carbon-based materials generally, has grown exponentially. Meanwhile in this increasingly-unstable climate, the Captain's been forced to remember real old winters – 1962-3 for example, when school shut down and he sledged down hillsides continuously, for weeks it seemed, on seaside ice, and his mother fed the birds in the little back garden as if her own life depended on it.

He remembers too, in the mid Sixties, his dad's horror as a relatively-new, small-town car-driver, on finding he had to join a Motorway. He remembers reading Rachel Carson's 'Silent Spring', in the days when the great fear for the environment was pesticides – a fear we seem now to have demoted, as if the problem were overcome. Not so many birds to feed now, Mum, whatever the weather. Wildlife programmes on the telly these days carry a strong whiff of nostalgia.

His was, yes indeed, doesn't he know it, the fortunate generation. His hard-working parents were well-educated (to age 14) and intelligent: they'd worked hard all their lives, worried about things far closer to hand than bombs or volcanoes, got through a War and continued to slave away in workplace and kitchen. Hopeful savings were eventually made or imagined to have been made, and only then prudent purchases: so that their modern Sixties children might achieve what their elders craved most for them – no longer just the war-generations' prefab Homes Fit for Heroes, but … qualifications; good, well-paid jobs; warm, comfortably-appointed homes.

And with this encouragement he and the other gannet-young, in cripplingly-expensive school uniforms as they grew, gaped their beaks and silently demanded to be filled – Now! Now! – with all the luxuries that their parents hadn't had since 1939: lots of good food (piping hot, fatty, salty, sugary please); consumer goods (his own wind-up watch! With a luminous dial! aged 10. A Brownie camera! at 11). And new home comforts (the family's first – black-and-white then, of course – television! at nearly 13).

His mother would eventually consent to get herself a fridge only in the 1980s, after he and his siblings had grown up and left home for good. She was never, ever, to bother with a washing machine, or use a launderette.

Yes, we, thinks the Captain, we – we did want all that new consumer stuff, no doubt; but also so much more. Our beaks yawned, our little feathered breasts fluttered for: Freedom; Liberation from conventional austerities and starved cravings; a Wonderful World in which everyone would be brothers and sisters; but – above all – Space away from home, to think our own new and different thoughts.

At least, that's what *he* remembers wanting back then.

And he remembers how shocked he was later when his cool proto-hippy university contemporaries suddenly (and this was ten years, nearly, before the Thatcher government) started to cut their hair again, and shine their shoes for the conventional jobs in the big, polluting, capitalist companies. Certainly, he in his turn shocked them, by the modesty of his material ambitions. Just as he shocks some now, by driving an old (not a new) motorhome. Just as he is himself shocked by people who own huge, double-axled new-built ones – to use them for less than two weeks of the year. They will point perhaps to his old wagon's carbon-consumption. He'll point to their conspicuous consumption of all things else.

Materialism was always the order of the day, certainly since the Industrial Revolution, and he can't see there's going to be much change to that. And obviously, the more Stuff we desire and consume, the more shit comes out as a by-product. Physically, materially, probably morally, the world must be going to hell in a handcart. He can't help thinking that driving this heavy van around he's giving his own shameful little shove to the retrograde rotations of ecological and spiritual progress. At the same time, he can't see himself doing a Thelma and Louise and driving Lotte off a cliff.

Well – but on the practical level what is The Good Life *now*? As a child, he was always attracted, through the grandparents' Methodist Chapel Sunday School, to the idea – even, maybe – of becoming a missionary! – or then, after rapid self-conversion to atheism, an Aid worker – in Africa. After all, his dad had been stationed for a time, that pre-operational training phase, in Kenya – then pronounced 'Keen-ya' – and he had always recalled the land glowingly: the plains, the kudu, the Masai, the sun-flattened trees, the distant white peak of Kilimanjaro... And yes, perhaps Kamper himself might still in his student years have gone to Africa – as his younger brother did, on VSO in Nigeria... had a different sort of missionary vocation to an inner-city Manchester comprehensive school's English department not taken him over instead. Back in the 1960s, the Good Life he'd been taught by Grammar School and Sunday School was always to do with Benefiting Society in some way. A sense that one must become a useful part of the world, of wider society: a molecule like one of the iron-filings sprinkled around a magnet in a grammar-school physics experiment, all pointing the right way.

In time (one wife and two children later, and having gained his adult position, place, duties and little local recognitions) he would come to realize that his only *real* ambition – through that impoverished, sheltered but idealistic time of his youth – had been: *just to become Real.*

More Real, and more In The Real World, than his parents in their quiet northern town had seemingly wanted to be for years – as if they, War or no War, had never had a real wider world to encounter, so assiduously did they seem to shun the possibility of a new one being available to them in their middle-age. A refusal to seek any change beyond some very small, unaccustomed, relative home-comforts; a slew of elderly relatives who required more (and it seemed to him more than their fair share) of it: all this made his parents seem more and more to live, not so much in the past, as in a sedated mush of predictable, dutiful repetition. By the time that the old grandparents and great-aunts – who had taken up from his teen-years onwards all his parents' time and emotional energy – fell away one by one, his dad had barely time left to start to be finally ill himself.

So throughout this phase, the no-longer-so-dutiful son kept his distance. Duties of his own. Education, education, education.

But the truth was, in that Real World to which he had gained entry and clung so self-righteously – those molecules had started pointing the opposite way. Molecules he'd thought he could always trust. First, a new election brought Margaret Thatcher: it was announced that there was no longer such a *real* thing at all as the Society in which he'd so recently brought himself to adulthood, and which along the way he thought he'd been trying to benefit. Get Real!

Second, there were lots of people, even in places like "progressive" Salford comps, who found it all too easy to align themselves as molecules in this entirely new field of market-forces. If you wanted to pursue your career and feed your growing family, you'd better learn to grow a face out of your arse too, or that new Boss would bite the honest one off.

And yes, third and most incomprehensibly (to him) of all at that time, in the middle of this – his young wife left for new adventures, leaving him with their two daughters age seven and four. So any other purpose would have to be put on the back-burner. It (or Society) was no longer what this real life was for. Looking after your family and being a father isn't moral or dutiful, but what you do without thinking (sometimes, it feels, without feeling, but with feelings in fact too deep for tears). A single working parent – that's enough Reality to be in, and to be, and so on, and so on.

In the midst of this his own father, Cyril, had wasted and died.

Clocks ticked, pages were turned and given grades. More ups and downs for himself than he'd care now to name, personally and professionally. And in the end it would be *two*, each ten-years-plus, marital relationships that were... over-and-done-with. And a third daughter. At that break-up, aged ten, Freya, unlike her sisters ten years before, stayed with her mother. Still to be supported financially, to think of and miss, and "do alternate weekends" with.

If he forces himself to think back now, and *tries* to put it all into an actual, factual, historical order – causes, effects – he just can't. It's a blur. It's a very bad blur. You know that feeling of blur, when you know you're going to cry and then you clamp down on it in order to Move, as briskly as possible, On? That blur.

How could *he* have been caught up in *that*? He'd always only tried to do the right thing! Maybe that was actually the problem.

* * *

But Hey. Come On – Now – seemingly this whole new life today – 2010 – in a whole new century, new millennium for god's sake, he has this new relationship (and how lucky is that, at his age?) with the Muse. And *three* beautiful, *independent,* now-very sorted, grown-up daughters. And after 30-odd years' work – but nonetheless suddenly – one chance appearing of an early redundancy-retirement package too good to refuse (especially given at the time the rather dodgy state of several aspects of his health).

Almost simultaneously, his dear old Mum finally died, of confused old age – leaving him, his two brothers and his sister a quarter each of the tiny scrap of cash she'd been allowed to keep, after they'd sold her tiny house so that she could be kept in that Home on the Cliff for her last years.

Hmm. Take a breath.

Take a break.

Take a look at the plastic horse. Life-size! And

"Don't marry her..."

Empedocles (?492 – ?432 b.c.e.) taught that, in our world, everything is *in* everything. And fundamentally there are simply Four Elements.

Earth,

Air,

Fire,

Water.

These four elements, he said, were the origins of all that is in and upon the earth, including human beings.

All these phenomena of our world – animate and inanimate – from rocks to wise men with beards – arise ultimately, he explained, in infinite combinations of these elements – and are continuously combined, broken down, re-combined, smashed to bits, sprout up again, die, fall apart… permanently disintegrating, perpetually reincarnating…

And that breaking and re-forming happens because they – we – are acted upon by (again, very simply) Two Forces.

Love.

And Strife.

Part Two

Portsmouth to Bilbao

… You have discovered of course
Only the Ship of Fools is
Making the voyage this year …

W.H.Auden – 'Atlantis' 1941

Chapter 8

So he's there, waiting for the boat. On the car-park, in their neighbouring lines, he has a chat with a couple of bikers his own age. They just got redundancy from a steel works near Glasgow. They're going to tour the Pyrenees, Spain, Portugal. One of them has a son in tow, in his late twenties.

"He's only just back in the saddle, hey Sam? Near enough wrote himself off last year, hey? Lost it on a corner up in fuckin Fyfe there – broke a bunch of ribs, punctured lung, gorra few pins in his leg. So no scootin' awa' on yir own, this trip kid, eh?"

He won't tell them about the Broken Ribs Trip. Small beer compared to that of yours, Sam. Not a motorbike crash. Though you've patched up pretty well. The limp now barely discernible in your leathered gait.

* * *

It's an advertised 'mini-cruise', for some passengers, the ferry from Portsmouth to Bilbao, there and back. This route, they're told, as they sail away from England between inscrutable parked destroyers and the Isle of Wight, can provide an excellent opportunity for whale-watching, depending on weather, tide and season. This means that even if there are no cetaceans in sight, small bunches of children can always be interested in joining an on-board group led by enthusiastic observers from Biscay Dolphin Research – for a few impatient minutes.

And the following day, today, even the experts have been having a thin time of it. And other entertainments on board are frankly, limited.

Lotte of course is stowed below, in wait for their onward expedition. When in conversation on land, or supported by her four wheels, he likes to stress his reasons for preferring to travel across the earth's surface in a motor vehicle, than above it in an aeroplane. After all, he'll say, flying by passenger-jet is really just time-travel.

But if ever, he mutters – later, twenty-four hours in to this thirty-six-hour "crossing" – if ever you wanted to *readjust* the point of view that surface-travel makes the most sense, then this "ferry" would be a useful starting-point. We joined the ferry to see the next bit of the world. But what did we see? We saw the sea – which offers no more visual variety than the oceans of sky-above-cloud for which we might have opted by boarding a plane. And it takes longer. Oh, immeasurably longer.

We saw the sea, he mutters again. Biscay, with all its reputation for storms, today is nonetheless flat, blue-grey. Not entirely the worse for that! Except that the very clarity of the day only exposes the unremitting *flatness* of what is on view. Thrumbling engines (and thank goodness we can hear and feel them – otherwise, today is so still, we'd feel we were lying literally becalmed) move us onward at a speed we must presume to be brisk enough for punctual arrival. But – a ferry? The point of a "ferry" is to hop you quickly across onto the nearest available land, be a substitute bridge or tunnel to take the nearest way from land to land. A ferry-boat's essence, surely, is squared-off extension of ramp, on which vehicles are briefly parked, drivers removed from their vehicles in temporary adherence to obscure-but-necessary health and safety issues, and then swiftly released again by fluorescent-jacketed unloaders onto continuous ramp-roadway.

He's sure they will dock on time – only tomorrow morning now – but Captain Kamper thanks goodness that he's not this vessel's Captain. What a way to spend your working life. To and fro. There and back. Over and over and over.

By now, resignation and boredom have settled in upon all the passengers. So this evening, some of them find their ways, as they did on the first night at the same time – into the remarkable, to him faintly-shocking, *Smoking Room* … It *is* shocking, even though he still regularly – he'll confess, there's plenty of time – smokes two, three or four cigarettes per night, wherever, pretty much, he finds himself. Maybe this is actually another inheritance from the Old Man. In the back of one of the war-photo albums is stuck the front of a "V Cigarettes" packet (V for Victory – made in India), and the tiny front flap of a book of "Soussa" (subtitled in Arabic) matches. Captioned, underneath, in that unmistakeable paternal hand:

"Necessities of Idleness".

He reckons from teenage memory that his dad, seldom "idle" in civvy street, still managed to smoke close on forty a day in the late Sixties to Seventies.

And nowadays, for himself, at home, most evenings – the Muse doesn't like it – he'll sit for a while in his den listening to the radio and blowing his smoke, however foul the night outside, whatever the season, out of the open window. At the pub in Leeds with his mate Roger once in a while they'll go and puff outside in a purpose-built, gazebo-esque garden-shelter equipped with a heater inside its roof that turns itself off impatiently before they've finished. In the van, he'll sit on the lowered door-step, or in a collapsible chair alongside.

And yet here on this ship thanks to the freedoms of technical extra-territoriality, he's offered the charms of that rebellious anachronism, a Smoking Room. It's established, or you might say retro-fitted, on Deck 8.

Here the Smokers sit. This as much as the Bingo Bar for'ard can be seen as the boat's downmarket hub. On this particular trip it's dominated by noisily-conversational forty-to-fifty-something, mostly-working-class Welsh couples. They're bulky, loud-laughing, dramatically-resigned people for whom an unlit space of cast-off saloon-bar furniture, torn and repaired with sticky-tape, is not apparently to be taken as a studied insult, but welcomed as a homely haven. He doubts if any of their local pubs are anything like so poorly-appointed. Except you can't smoke in them – but then again, you *can* buy a drink... Though signs, unremoved from over a set of permanently-closed bar-shutters, indicate that this was once "The Truckers Bar", the divorce between vices is retained.

There are very few tables. This is a repository both of ill-fitting cast-off furniture, and of people, charity-shop-random. He sits in a bay of disintegrating red leatherette banquettes that might seat eight backsides, surrounding one low, inadequate, paper-cup-festooned little table – just drop your tab into that half-finished paper-cup of flat Coca Cola when you've finished. The next table's been replaced entirely – by a rusty old red metal brandy-bowl-shaped ash-goblet about three feet in diameter, full almost to the brim with several trips'-worth of dimps and ash scattered on sand. A veritable fag-ash fountain.

He's been reading (but doesn't pollute its pages by bringing it along with him to a shameful pit of addiction) Julian Barnes' "Nothing To Be Frightened Of" – a living memoir and meditation upon a lifetime's interest in the question of death. Desperately, doggedly and with humour, Barnes seeks the meaning of mortality, as considered from the perspective of later life – more specifically, his search at sixty years old for the meaning of his own inevitable demise at some unspecifiable future date. The Captain has a good idea what Barnes would make of him and his Smoking Room companions. Few of them resemble the writers or philosophers whose perceptions of mortality that fine writer compares with those of his own upper-middle-class parents or siblings.

Anyway here we all are, he thinks, the Smokers, still sitting waiting for disembarkation tomorrow upon a foreign shore, after a period too uneventful to be experienced as short. Joking. Laughing too loud. Putting in time before – Bingo? Exiting periodically to put money in a couple of fruit-machines on the landing outside. Or simply, and more singly – in the Captain's case – staring into smoky space. Light, puff, stare, stub out, sit beyond all purpose of sitting, stand wearily before finally moving on, in hope of finding activity more purposeful, less compulsive, elsewhere aboard.

They are all Barnes' people though. Bodily they illustrate the commonality of lives at a certain age, presented raw, without *bon mots* or syllogisms. They've become a silent movie, as it were, or a video backdrop:

"hanging on in quiet desperation is the English way"[1].

He won't split hairs, that many of his companions here aren't English. Nationality, or gradations of it, are irrelevant in the face of That. (In any case, half his own ancestors were Welsh, if you go back a couple of centuries.)

He's put in mind of one of the Circles of Hell – or at least of a minor corridor in Purgatory – from Dante; or of that Mariner of Coleridge's

"alone, alone on a wide, wide sea"

Rationally, the ship is moving; quickly enough, and rolling slightly too; yet this motion, coupled with the difficulty of imagining in any real way arrival at any real destination, still leaves him feeling becalmed, beset. And all

---

[1]   'Time' from Dark Side of the Moon Pink Floyd 1973

possible character-types, any guessed-at capacities for reflection, are fogged away as a smoke-cloud ship's community – everyone starts losing definition, weight, solidity.

The whole boatload, wherever they are – on "observation deck", in cinema, in cafe or already in row-upon row of cabins like his for a second night soon in the windowless bowels – all of them are just waiting, putting in time. Can he exclude from this consideration the officers and crew? Well, most of *them* seem to be either standing bored behind a bar, or still pushing the last trip's laundry-trolley.

Waiting, you might say, yes, Julian, to die.

"I had not thought death had undone so many."

Obviously they should all be reading. Resolving to lift his spirits he goes back to the smokeless decks, puts away Barnes for later and instead looks out his "Travels with Charley": the first travel book he ever read, and certainly, the one for this moment. Opening at an early page reminds him how much John Steinbeck loved sailing-boats: so that when – contemplating the epic road trip back in 1960, before any Recreational Vehicle (RV) industry had been established in the States – he had commissioned

"a little house built like the cabin of a small boat"

custom-built onto a modest truck-chassis. What's more, it was aboard four-wheeled "Rocinante" that Steinbeck wore his distinctive cap:

"one I have worn for many years, a blue serge British naval cap with a short visor, and on its peak the lion and unicorn, as always fighting for the crown of England".

This cap was a trophy of his WW2 service – as a late-joining war correspondent – given to him by a British MTB Captain on whose craft he had set off from the south coast of England to North Africa in 1943. Significantly, it later came to be Steinbeck's opinion that the man who gave it to him was

"a gentle gentleman, and a murderer"

because his vessel had later been sunk, with all hands, while the skipper held back momentarily from destroying a German E-boat.[2]

Steinbeck, though, had always loved tales of chivalric combat, knightly deeds. "Rocinante" was Don Quixote's horse. A leisure sailor after the War, he named his yacht, medievally, "The Fair Eleyne", for his wife and muse, Elaine. Yet this twentieth-century Laureate understood better than most the difficulty of applying "chivalrous" ethical standards in modern times, especially in modern warfare. That he continued to wear that particular Captain's cap showed him owning and honouring the moral ambiguities that are always present in his novels. Could the Torpedo-boat's Captain simply be regarded as a "murderer" (of his own men) for momentarily "sparing" an opponent in combat?

So anyway, it's also out of admiration for the classic 1962 US travelogue that the 2010 Captain, aboard his Lotte, has wryly invested himself with the rank – of course also thanks to a lorry-driver's reminder. He doesn't sport naval-type headgear himself, though he's met plenty of camper-vanners who do – and perhaps they do it also, who knows, in Steinbeck's honour.

But – even an *imaginary* Captain's cap – well, if it's a mark of self-honour, an echo of Laureateship, it's also a recognition of conscious fallibility. If you accept "rank" and responsibility, you take on vulnerability to unanswerable moral riddles. Kindness, or moral hesitation, can have bitter consequences, he knows for himself well enough. If the cap fits...

Coincidentally, the first thing the Grand Old Man did, on setting out on his trip back in '62 was to drive onto a ferry – the relatively-short trip to his mainland, across Long Island Sound – and there he'd spotted some of the US Navy's nuclear submarines –

"armed with mass murder, our silly, only way of deterring mass murder" –

based nearby at New London. On the boat he talked to a young fellow who had experience of nuclear subs. The young submariner was gently positive about them:

---

2   "Travels With Charley" – John Steinbeck, 1962 – Penguin Classics reprint 2000 pp 6, 32.

(No doubt the British skipper had wanted to capture the boat "alive" for intelligence-gathering purposes – most of the small number of German "enigma" type coding machines that ended up at Bletchley Park had been obtained from captured U- and E-boats.)

"And could be he's right and I'm wrong. It's his world, not mine any more,"

concedes the great man.

As he wrote this in 1960, John Steinbeck was fifty-eight years old. The Captain was nine years old in that year, and is fifty-eight in this one… (Don Quixote, surprisingly, wasn't even fifty. But Cervantes was fifty-eight when he wrote the end of his story.)

His fellow-passengers still sit in suspended animation. At first glance, you have to discount from this, he thinks, the returning coach-load of teenage Spanish schoolchildren. What *they're* waiting for, is the last chance for their Concita or Alonso, over there by the door, to come across. In their dreams. Meanwhile, they'll clog up the corners of stairways, and stare glue-eyed across conversations, toward the Unattainable One. They're resigned, too, and waiting – then throw in an occasional, desperately-active, hurtling shriek around the decks with The One Friend Who Understands (girls) – or (boys) a smirking guffaw with the rest of the Crazy Lads – waiting, waiting for the end of this agonised adolescence. (It'll never come, kids.)

When he lands tomorrow in Bilbao and resumes a traveller's identity, Captain of his own destiny he tells himself, it'll also be in a focussed attempt to shake off Lethe's ferry and the sense of communal sleepwalk towards rotating knives. Purposes – purposes even spurious, dreamlike, pre-demented – determined purposes, must be followed. Events. Please, may something eventually Happen. Oh, for god's sake, get him off this boat and onto land where he can place his feet, turn his wheels, create a direction, follow an impulse, fulfil a Plan. Even be taken by surprise, so long as it's not a bad one.

He'll need to fill Lotte's tank when they've landed, or within 100km or so, and wonders what diesel prices'll be like in Spain. He wants to calculate his costs ahead of time if he can. Those distances he's committed to! They're starting now to look more and more colossal.

Still, he reckons, over his road-atlas: tomorrow just get across that top bit of Spain, and camp near Biarritz. That's into France at least, and enough driving (on the Right – he'll need to get used to that again too) for the first day. Careful now.

Part Three

Northern Spain, Southern France

The past is never dead. It's not even past.

William Faulkner, Requiem for a Nun

Chapter 9

Ariege – evening arrival – morning discombobulation – calm down

Ah. Oh. OK.

So... instead of stopping off in Biarritz, it seems he's determinedly driven (or fled) in that one day, more than 400 kilometres – and has thus arrived at the edge of a favourite part of France, the *département* of Ariège.

Not far south of Toulouse nor north of the Pyrenees, and close to the prehistoric caves of Niaux and Mas d'Azil, in previous years he and the Muse have stayed in Lotte near here a couple of times, once with his broken ribs. They've explored underground and atop mountains, have walked and swum – toured, sat still and always eaten well. It's a land of small towns, kind greetings, graceful panoramas. *Les Ariègeois* seem to combine the South's friendliness with the careful reserve of all hill-peoples.

This camp-site open here is new to him (and it's early season, after all). It offers a small bar, and even – a nice surprise, though in a way you *might* expect it round here after all, he tells himself – its little 'Restaurant' properly does deserve the name. This is France, after all. But he's more tired than hungry. So: having mooched around, hands in pockets, in order to feel for tonight that he owns the place and its view across the valley to the blue mountains; and having read on the notice-board that they've started reintroducing native brown bears on the remoter fringes of those dark slopes; he goes in, orders a little beer, looks at the menu, forgives them the presence there of pizza among the options (it *is* a campsite) and orders: just a starter – home-made paté – not in his experience a staple of English campsites. The bearded brother of a bulky, clean-shaven proprietor brings it to him at the bar, with three different homemade breads. Gastronomically, not a bad start to the expedition-proper. Soon he's forgotten what else he ate today... and yesterday... and indeed every day since he was last in this proudly, confidently gastronomical *pays*.

He's on his way! Thank goodness for effortless, classy southern France.

The following morning, though, becomes his first foreign-campsite-getting-up of the trip. Much anticipated, already it feels very different. *That* – yesterday's drive and the food on arrival – was a completed achievement.

This – this morning – challenges, and asks questions.

As though they're working shifts in conspiracy with the Spanish group on the boat, there's a party of French school-kids on site, maybe 13-14 year olds. Last night, they were running around and screaming until about 1am. This morning, early, they're already screaming again (female) or loudly and endlessly bouncing a football while shouting (male). In England, other kids would call them "chavs". They're mostly wearing those tracksuit-bottoms with stripes down the side or a trade-mark across the bum. He used to teach kids like these and so he feels a confusingly-nostalgic affection for them, combined with irritation and frustration. Don't they understand where they are? Don't they understand people are asleep? Isn't there anyone in charge, to tell them the way to behave around other people on a campsite? Etc, etc.

He's thin-skinned. He'd forgotten – now he's remembering – that camping abroad continues at every step to force you to be alive, sensitive, mindful and careful of yourself in an alien environment where, with your French once again rusty, you're not always immediately going to read the signs. And as a single traveller you can't 'check in' about things with a companion. You can easily get stuff out of proportion.

So he needs just to understand that he's grumpy, and jumpy.

After last night's outstanding supper, irritatingly, the coffee, milk and bread he has on board all feel a bit stale. The van's fridge has actually worked too efficiently: so the butter's refrigerated too hard. And he's been stowing things away inefficiently. That'd be just about all right if he were only away for the weekend; soon enough they'd be unloaded again back into the house.

But this is different. This is a real expedition! It's nearly a year since his last one. He must get a good on-the-road routine established – and everything stowed, so that it doesn't slide, roll or crash as he corners – no, nothing did, yesterday, but still…

All of this is underlined by a failure to stow *himself* properly. He actually left a skylight tilted up and open last night! The spring evening was still warmish when he turned in at ten; all the same, experience should tell him to shut all the windows, since a van cools down pretty sharply. So it got colder a bit more quickly in his sleeping-bag, and amplified the French kids' racket....

After a while, he's eaten the stale bread, and done a lot more bumbling and muttering. Though Lotte has gone very well to get him here on the first day's drive and is behaving just fine, he must check oil and water before setting off. But that'll put him further *behind!* Last night he planned to be half-an-hour down the road by now. Another full day's slog and he could get to Avignon by tonight, or Arles, or Aix. Maybe he'll still manage it; he doubts it somehow.

On the other hand, *yesterday* morning he'd expected only to be at Biarritz by now: and then he'd had that sudden sense of release and elation to be Away! It had spurred him forward and on. So that's already put him several hours *ahead* of himself, he might say.

Ahead? Behind? Stop it. He's not made a detailed schedule or calendar of this trip, and doesn't intend to. He makes himself more coffee from the bit he's got left in the tin – that means he'll work his way into the fresher stuff sooner. Maybe that's what he was doing with the driving yesterday. Trying to get away from the stale and into the fresh and bright ...

Now try to do the same thing with this morning's head.

But in a wash of contradictory feelings from everywhere and nowhere, suddenly nothing matters to him so much as family – the alive, now, Family he actually does things with and for. His partner, the beautiful Muse – still works: is at work, now, right now, this morning, he can be sure, while he's still maundering into this mug. Their next few years together, their late fifties, early sixties, need plotting out, need planning, and better than this unfocused, silly trip. What's he doing, here, on his own – on his own on a bloody campsite, suddenly – well no, not suddenly at all! – more than a thousand miles away from everyone he cares about, from anything he needs to be doing, from anyone he needs to be reaching...?

Even though he knew this moment of panic was always there – waiting to be reached as it always is at some point on a solo trip – now he's flapping like a shredded tyre. Only to be expected but: disorientated; homesick; time-and-motion-sick.

And what if – what if there *is* another predictable, disastrous Big Brother Icelandic explosion? Yes, yes, he can worry about that again now – a disaster that will leave him as nothing better than a guilt-ridden escapee. He's *voluntarily* driving away from home, alone, away from the Muse, away from being able to Help If Something Happens.

It wasn't just that ferry boat, was it? Because now here he is adrift, agoraphobic in his van.

Not for the first time, but this time for some reason feeling more alone than ever. Irrational fears. But irrational, this trip. Does he always feel this way? Selfish? Pathetic? Probably. But of course, fuelled by Guilt. About what?

Oh, stop it. Calm down. There *is* a sensible, steady Plan.

OK: so one lovely daughter's soon getting married; another's already four-months-happily-pregnant; the third, a few short months from starting university: bride and two bridesmaids they'll be, along with another friend of the bride's, in Sorrento. Yes, so ditch all the Strife and have a whale of a time meeting up with them – be harmoniously content, in Love with life.... It's an adventure. Get in the mood.

But that wedding's in a *month's* time! He *should* still be at home, just planning, like them, to *fly* out, a couple of days before the wedding … Instead, he's "planned" – oh, he'd better review it, get his head straight, check how much time he's really got, and if – and this is the point – if he *should* *really* be doing it:

- a drive from Bilbao across France to the Alps

- via the Italian Lakes, to Florence (a meeting with old friends Mike and Meg and their van for a couple of days)

- a meandering drive down through central Italy, via the Muse's friends Tina and Bill's house, and

- on, down to the southern parts, using the special map on which he has numbered, ringed in pen, certain places relating to his father's War

- ferry across the strait, drive to Trapani, the westernmost edge of Sicily – one of his dad's targets, and the budget-flight airport at which he'll collect daughter Number 3 (Bridesmaid No2)

- then take her back across the island to visit Mount Etna, and up again into southern Italy,

- to a hotel in Sorrento on the Bay of Naples, where they will meet daughters Number 1 (pregnant) and Number 2 (to be wed) and (among the trickier guests) their mother, his long-divorced partner Number 1....

- do the ceremony, have a party

- and finally, with luck, connect up again with the Muse, who will have flown out to Perugia, then back to Tina and Bill's and a bit of touring....

- before back up through France and finally Zeebrugge, Hull, home.

And – But – Look at him now! Three days in. So what sort of state will he be in by *then*?

It all seemed like a good idea at the time ...

He'll have driven Lotte 1,700 miles at least to the end of Sicily, entirely alone, before he picks up Freya. And then he'll drive back with her another five hundred miles to the wedding, then eventually after a few days with the Muse drive back home through France and Belgium and hop across to Hull. What's that – another 1,200 miles? Add in the detours. Three and a half thousand miles, give or take. In a heavy eighteen year-old vehicle. He's one day, in effect, into that whole trip; and feeling old and tired. He's one day into the trip; and feeling vain and vague. He's one day into the trip; and he's already fairly sure he's bitten off more than he can chew. The whole thing is one big, old, mad mistake. It's not as if he's *young* any more.

And... He's pretty sure it's not just the wedding that has him in this state. Bad light in the sky again ... Smoke? Ash? Is he imagining it? What to do?

What else? Keep driving. Oh, God. This really is the middle of nowhere, the start of a trip to somewhere several steps too far, too strong, too emotionally dangerous. Bombing results good ...

Too bloody silly. Too bloody on his own. Too Big For His Boots!

Not that he can bale out now.

Chapter 10

*A singular note – dreams present and past – a burst of flame – a nuclear age
– preventing catastrophe – saved by a saying – family likenesses*

At first, he thought it was one of the lorry-drivers whistling to his mate.
You don't sleep as well on these French Autoroute *aires* as you would in a
campsite, but they are free, and ideal to pull up on after a motorway slog.
Lotte'd trundled in that night between a huge blue Italian wagon pulling a
double-trailer, and a French rig in canary yellow.

And now, much later, it was very dark in here (all blinds drawn, skylights
closed and doors locked tight, but he knew it was still not light outside) –
when he heard – it woke him from a nightmare, as if a part of it – a deep,
solitary whistle, almost a phrase of a tune. And then just once, repeat...

Now he began to know that footpads of the sort the Caravan Club Books
always warn you of in these places were exchanging their secret message,
before closing in on Lotte with sledgehammers, before breaking in, stealing
his wallet, credit cards, identity – perhaps, even worse, his coffee – and
leaving him bleeding in a ditch....

After a minute's absurd waking panic – of frantic, frozen listening – there
– repeated and immediately ornamented upon, that single human-sounding
note was evidently – the first bird of the dawn chorus! He's never heard *that
one bird* before, or if he has, he's never known it...

He feels cold. Silly funk, and he's chilled somewhere in the back. Where....
OK, south of Lyon somewhere, how far north of Avignon? Tired last night.
It's four a.m. The sun may be rising, somewhere. If so, it's caught in a haze
of cloud.

The too-familiar sense of waking from bad, unremembered dreams. He thought he'd swept away all the old fright with yesterday's good drive, for a while had left behind the feeling that driving long distance on featureless roads was just running away… What's real, what's not? Dreams he can't call back now are still there somewhere, like a malfunctioning vid, a black seascape in the back of his mind. He hadn't wanted to wake up to *this* bad feeling, ever again. Education, culture, literature, have only been able to help him to label more accurately what feels an *inborn* dread: an infant-school-version of the bleak twilight on Matthew Arnold's "Dover Beach",

'where ignorant armies clash by night.'

That's where his head is now. Other times, it's the desert birds circling the 1919 Yeats' Beast,

'his hour come round at last'

slouching to be born: as the totalitarian era – a century of collective brutality, including that War of his dad's. Heat-shimmer, dirty wing-ripples under the murk of his morning mind, all *Anima Mundi* and ash-clouds.

Aged – what – seven? Eight? He had that dream. Almost his earliest remembered dream. Of

going down to the Green, as they called the local patch of grass – to play cricket. Elder brother Sid, down on one knee, Boy-Scout-tracker-like, spotting a mark, a crack in the earth (as often appears in hard-baked earth in summer) and stating certainly "This mark means there's going to be a Burst Of Flame!" and hurrying him back up the hill – to get indoors.

Horripilation. Even now his body's trying to shudder it away from him.

A rapid collapse of time. Knowledge now, that the Burst of Flame has taken place, outside, but it's had no physical effect upon those within… Stunned realization – his family's small white dog (not a waking reality) got left outside, unquestionably has been incinerated. Mum's there, Dad's not. Grandma, Mum's frail old mother, is there on her knees in the hallway – as she normally would be, first thing in the morning, at her actual fireplace; but now – shovelling up ashes that have broken through the wall… next to the cupboard under the stairs.

Cupboard-under-the-stairs: where a pal's mum once told him she hid in the War when the siren sounded. That can't have happened very often in that town, but his own mother never sounded completely sure all that was in the past; and through ·all his post-war, Cold War childhood, the town's air-raid siren was still there, like a big cotton-reel on a tall pole, at the top of their road – he remembers it was regularly tested.

As an adult brought back often to that dream, he's come to the conclusion that in the 1950s, in his own child-mind place somehow, he must have been aware of the Bomb. That *must* have been it. But how? He has no specific recollection of being told what such a device actually was, and what it might in fact do, until much later, in the Sixties, at grammar-school – in a Science-lesson.

A special, one-off educational film? In a black-and-white film, a blackened, white city-scape. And a white shadow of a vaporised human being, printed into a black wall.

"Describe what happened how you will, the effect you will have is severely-limited. Our minds are not yet attuned to such large dimensions. We have no mental standard by which to discriminate between a million degrees of

heat, and ten million. To try and visualize it would be a waste of time. We might just as well agree that the Bomb is bigger than our understanding, and not worry about finding out how much bigger. We would do far better, I think, to concern ourselves with the question of how human nature reacts to the fact of its existence ..."[1]

"...I could tell you of the most extraordinary sensation I have ever felt.... How, after the first blinding flash we snatched off our polarized glasses and saw a grotesque ball of fire, half a mile in diameter, rocketing upwards at a rate of 20,000 feet a minute. How even from twenty-five miles away, we clutched hold of our safety-belts as the blast-waves hit us, the first from the explosion itself, and the second reflected from the ground. How three minutes later, from a height of three and a half miles above the earth, we stared upward at a vast, boiling, incandescent cloud that reached a full twenty thousand feet above us.

"I could talk, too, of the impression of absolute physical power that the spectacle presented.... Its form is perfect symmetry. It gives the appearance of infinite control. Its every movement demonstrates the law of equal and opposite reaction. It is utterly unique. You cannot watch it without a sensation of overpowering, breathless awe.

"Then I could describe the effect of the bomb on its target. How the town was obliterated by a volcanic pyramid of smoke four miles in diameter. How at a range of thirty miles we could actually see particles of dust and dirt being sucked 10,000 feet and more into the air. How, in a matter of minutes, houses in the opposite part of the town from the scene of the explosion burst into flames, from no other cause than sheer heat. How twenty-two hours later, a photo-reconnaissance plane turned back, because the target was still obscured.[12]

Another image, unrelated yet related, comes back periodically and has haunted him since – when? – when did he first see pictures of those tragic, ash-preserved bodies at Pompeii? Possibly it *was* in the family's four-volume encyclopaedia "The World of the Children", with its black-and-white "plates". Also including: Vesuvius in eruption, possibly Etna too. This was

[1]   Leonard Cheshire: Account as observer of atomic bombing of Nagasaki, 1945. BBC Sound Archive, 1947

what might happen. Cracks in the earth *could* explode. There are bursts of flame – and Bursts of Flame. The Mark is Upon the Earth.

So he actually grew up with a sense that one day he might have to *do* something. Not just run. Now, in fact, he's running towards it! When his parents started to "have a row" he used, as a child, to hide. But if it became unbearable, he used to run into the middle of it, to stop it.

Oh, heck.

The Captain generally, as you can well imagine, keeps all this very much to himself; and in normal life, is distracted from it the same as others – a but he's still at heart that child. He's always had a very strong imagination – so, what if this – this thing in Iceland – is only the *start of a full season* of European volcanic activity? Like Lisbon –Iceland 1755? Suppose he drove down to Naples or Messina, just in time to be buried in the final eruption from Vesuvius or Etna that brings an end to Life As We Know It? The earthquake at l'Aquila was only last year. Why does it not feel *entirely* incredible that he might end up as a compressed-ash Pompeii-cast-statue of a man who refused to let go of his coffee-mug?

Don't be so bloody absurd.

But for some reason *this* trip is starting to be about *Everything*: about parents, children, bombs, volcanoes, cracks in the earth, fire. Love, Strife. All those leaking stories. Buried terrors of known secrets. Always the nagging, portable fear: of failing to save the day, shown up as too big for his boots. All inherited – or learned so early. Is he going off his head? Well as ever, he's giving himself a very sporting chance of doing so.

But "Let's get some light on the subject," he hears his Father proverbialising: "Let the dog see the rabbit". It's too early in the morning for all this. He squirms the sleeping-bag and turns on his bulkhead lamp. And of course, now, it *is* all paranoia, produced systematically and in order, as usual, by figments. Memory, imagination... A great start to the day, and at… 4.30am. Ptcha.

The birds are now really warming to their work. He half-dresses to visit the toilet behind the multi-lane petrol-stand. He makes a coffee, discovers he's ravenous, eats breakfast cereal and milk, puts his feet up – and sleeps, for another three hours.

When he wakes up again, he's in full sunlight, though the trucks on either side of him still haven't moved. Now it's 8.15. And look, two cars have parked beside him during that second instalment of shut-eye, and two sets of French kids are playing energetically together on the swings: looks as if this could be the only time in the day the weather'll be cool enough for them to do so. The two young couples, pairs of parents, are chatting together smoking and drinking coffee, bums pressed onto warm car-wings next to open doors; letting a bright, fresh morning into their cramped, stuffy travel-capsules; stretching their legs, having made an early start to beat the traffic out of town. A little holiday mini-*convoi*. All very happy, jovial, well-balanced, confident.

Although now in one sense he feels even more alone, it's much better than before. In dancing, dazzling background trees, the local birdlife is by now improvising its full-strength orchestration.

He takes a big deep breath, and exhales it, smiling. That's what daylight's for. It tells you, Day is real. Night is not. It lets the dog see the rabbit.

Family: its history, its language. Today, driving, he'll try to make a full collection of old parental phrases, none of which ever implied any sort of belief that the world might ever be an ecstatically happy place, or that you ever might Live the Dream and it might well come true! Instead these sayings cast about them a sensible, stoical, if rather deadening Common Sense: designed to make you put yourself and your life Into Proportion. He still meets those weary old household gods as they actually speak from his own mouth; or more often, as today, inside his head:

anything for a quiet life
it's for your own benefit
too big for your boots
that's hard lines
get some light on the subject
let the dog see the rabbit
perhaps it's all for the best
could be worse

Poor old Mum: she could laugh at herself, later. Would tell the story of having a bad day and taking her four-year-old youngest to the shops in the rain. Responding to her sighing – "Oh Dearie Me" – his little brother had said: "Never mind Mummy, soon be worse". These days she twinkles affectionately at him from within the classical features of his youngest daughter, Freya. Whenever she does so, there's loving pleasure for him in the new recognition.

Tomorrow morning, though, his Dad will glance back at him, appraisingly, for an instant – in the mirror above the basin. This is less comforting. Prematurely-lined, and much more deeply-wrinkled than other folk, he was – and now *he* is. Father – and son.

He'll keep the driving gentle today. Next overnight stop might be … maybe around Gap?

Chapter 11

Foothills – not quite a meeting – usefulness? – "Ops" – the wrong diagonal –
223 & the North African endgame Jan-May 1943

At the late-afternoon, wooded site, after a modest drive but still somewhat a-weary, he places himself outside his van in a collapsible canvas chair ("Executive", it calls itself on the label, on account of a little netting pocket in the right-hand armrest, for a drink to be slumped).

He's beside a hedge dividing his from the next door pitch. An English couple. They arrived just after him. Steadfastly they have failed to look up, twice, from book and newspaper respectively, at his walking by. They'll know from his number-plate that he's English too. In fact, he reasons, it's overwhelmingly-likely that his registration-plate had a great deal to do with their choice of berth: Let's park here to be beside another English van (containing, we naturally assume, another English couple) because proprieties will be observed and there'll be No Speaking Over The Hedge Unless Spoken To.

So of course, quite capable of being English himself, the Captain obliges. Now he sits with his beer, his road-atlas and his evening cigarette not six feet away from them through the greenery. In this hour spent in their neighbouring "gardens", he'll overhear just one single interaction between his compatriots.

HE: I'm going in now. I'll put away this chair now.

SHE: *something inaudible*

HE: I'm going to have some cheese and bikkits.

Something inaudible

Cheese and bikkits – *(he goes in)*

For some reason, the Captain decides they're from Penge.

It's all part of the nonsense that travelling can make of you.

* * *

By the end of the following day, he's continued to belt westwards, up into the foothills of the Alps. He has to get on, to leave All That behind. He needs, as always, to become more Real. Views become magnificent. The kilometres steadily tick on, dusk begins to fall and headlights to glit more brightly. All he has asked, is to be on this road. It wasn't a lot to ask – yet it was, very much: that he might be on this road, and making it real to himself, and himself more real in the process.

Keep going. Keep Go-ing.

What is there to do but Go? Don't plan, don't plot.

Just, Go.

And anyway – what's the use of the older man, when his children, grown-up, have flown the coop, and the workplace has coughed him up? Well, he has to be somebody *to himself*, once he's stopped being somebody for them. In the circumstances it seems a bad joke that, now he has time to notice and work on his *own* habits and idiosyncrasies, he'll often find himself speaking his father's words, and almost it feels out of his father's very mouth: catch a shadow of that walk, the elbows turned a little out; the quizzical raised eyebrow in the driving mirror.

He smiles somewhat bitterly in recognition at the joke life's playing.

Let's have some light on the subject.

You gotta laugh. Laugh or cry.

* * *

In 1943, Cyril, aged 26 had become a full-time turret-twisting cog of 223 Squadron, Desert Air Force (officially NATAF, the Northwest African Tactical Air Force). The role of this force was close air-support for the Eighth

Army's fight-back across the deserts of Egypt, Libya[1] and Tunisia – against the Afrika Korps under Rommel, who until late 1942 had "owned" North Africa. Now, though, the battle of El Alamein had just been fought and won. Monty was the new hero back home. The tide was said to be turning. The chase was on.

After his

      Ops5 as briefed   Wadi Akeret

Cyril noted in his log for the first time:

                              …1 a/c lost.

The lost crew was from their twin Baltimore outfit, Squadron 55, with whom some planes were shared for Ops purposes. Squadron Records show Baltimore IIIa no.193 as the aircraft destroyed (two parachutes were seen, but the whole crew were posted as "missing", the plane having exploded). Bob Connell and his crew had in fact flown that very same plane, earlier on the very same day, over the very same target...

And then, five days later:

      7.2.43   Crashed on t/off ------------→ NIL FLYING

Baltimores apparently always had a tendency to "nose-over" on take-off.

But Cyril's version of this event – as just once, later, he would recount, in explanation of a couple of photographs, warped and fading in his album – was that they'd been forced to follow the orders of a new "Brass Hat", visiting for the day. Taking off cross-wind, as they often would, he'd set them off in line-astern, but on the "wrong" diagonal. This meant that they were blinded by the rest of the squadron's dust – which probably didn't improve engine-performance either – all in all, the absolute opposite result to that intended by proper desert ground formation.

So anyway, realising they'd been on the ground too long and were likely to crash, he'd wedged his shoulders and elbows against the gun-turret's metal collar and then locked his fingers against the back of the bulky steel gunsight inches from his nose-end, thus protecting, as best he might, his skull from bouncing like a football between rocks and hard places if impact occurred.

---

1   Libya was the first territory in history to become subject to aerial bombardment in war. A Turkish camp at Ain Zara near Tripoli was bombed from Italian airships in 1911. Coincidentally, almost a hundred years later, Ain Zara had become the location of Ghadafi's most notorious prison and torture-centre.

At the runway's end, Bob Connell caught the top of a stone boundary-wall with his undercarriage, and one wheel was forced right up through its engine-nacelle as they hit the deck on the other side in a wrenching belly-flop.... When it all went quiet and the rest of the planes had gone, and dust settled, 2,000lbs of high-explosive was of course still right there, under their feet, and a full load of fuel in either wing. One imagines they got out pretty quickly.

However, given that the whole thing *hadn't* blown it's clear they went back and took photographs (above) and the ground-crew set to work lifting and salvaging. These snaps are still to be found in a little plush-cushion-covered album commercially-entitled "My Photo Souvenirs of War" with a pretty little palm-tree on the front, which Cyril would later bring home to the folks. What's the point, he and his mates might well have said, of having risked your neck, led by buffoons, in a crate full of TNT, if you can't prove afterwards – if only to yourself – that it really happened? Otherwise these might sound suspiciously like tall tales.

Even to yourself. "Live to tell the tale". Is that, the Captain wonders, "Live, and as a result, be able to tell the tale"? Or "Live, in order to"?

Through the spring and summer of 1943, squadrons 55 and 223 took regular losses of aircraft and personnel. Meanwhile it was with their support that the Eighth Army pushed the German *Afrika Korps* back, step by step – and in the Desert Air-Force's case it was hop by hop, from hastily-improvised desert air-strips – from that turning-point at El Alamein, through Libya and Tunisia. In later life, Cyril could roll North African place-names off his tongue like date-stones: Mersa Matruh, Sidi Barani, Benghazi, Enfidaville, Bou Ficha – exotically toothsome ingredients in a traveller's, rather than a warrior's, tale.

Ultimately, on the 11th of May, 1943, Montgomery's military machine ratcheted the Axis forces right back upon Tunis – and onto the oncoming American 5th Army, newly-deployed from Casablanca. At Tunis, on that day, a prodigious catch of 200,000 German and Italian troops surrendered to the Allies.

Two incidents from this, the final stage of the Allies' victorious campaign in North Africa, sum up in their detail a great deal about the Eighth Army and its air-support. [2]

Firstly, from Christopher Lee – later Hammer Films' Count Dracula, and even later Saruman in 'Lord Of The Rings'[3] – who served with Nos 37 and 260 (fighter-bomber) Squadrons as Intelligence Officer. He recounted how, when his squadron were driving in their trucks towards Tunis through the "Gabes Gap" – scene of brutal fighting, and in fact a huge missed opportunity by the Eighth Army to cut off and destroy the Axis force – Lee had to do his best to distract his group of pilots from the appalling carnage, which their ground-attack Kittyhawks had had their share in dealing out, and which now was to be seen all around them:

'He didn't want it weighing too heavily on their consciences. Air combat tended to be an impersonal affair. It was the plane or truck, not the individual flying or driving it. It was best to keep it that way.'

Shortly after this, Nigel Nicolson[4], then in the First Army's Guards' Brigade, saw Montgomery climb on a pile of rubble and address such people of

---

[2]   Both anecdotes below are quoted from: James Holland, 2005. *Together We Stand*. Harper Collins

[3]   – acting in the Hobbit film of 2011 at almost 90 years old.

[4]   – later MP, publisher, writer, biographer.

Sousse as could be rounded up to "listen" – a coastal town almost completely destroyed by Allied bombing, with civilian casualties of course never counted – and how he

> 'told the people how glad they must be to have been liberated by the famous Eighth Army … I hated Monty from that moment'.

The Captain checks his dad's Log again. By the time of the historic German surrender at Tunis, Cyril had flown a mere fifteen sorties. He'd have to fly fifty-seven more before they let him go home.[5]

---

[5]   In Joseph Heller's 'Catch-22', the number of missions required (also in the Italian theatre) by the USAAF keeps increasing, while crew-men get tantalisingly-closer to advertised upper limits only to see them repeatedly increased. Heller himself flew 60. Bob Connell and his crew all flew more than 70.

Part Four

Italy

There are no foreign lands. It is only the traveller who is foreign.

Robert Louis Stevenson: 'The Silverado Squatters'

Chapter 12

Fréjus – clouds – Anson – Airfix – discretion and deviousness – attention &
ignoring – tangentiale Torino – planes & pilots – the Man.

On the journey, along the road, as narrators like Defoe and Fielding understood, truth will out, in fits and starts. Sometimes, thinks the Captain, the unfolding of a road is at one and the same time the unfolding of his mind into a labyrinth, careless of the rearward unravelling of its thread. What trails behind him, a tale still attached to the teller but perhaps no longer to the rock at the cave-opening, may prove not much use on the way back out.

Sometimes "The Road" then, is only the next bend, distant, looming, gone and replaced by the next. Sometimes the road in the head becomes the road of the gut and the lifeline. Unplotted, apparently clueless, simply it is the story; the road that has been taken; and sometimes a new road can become the road to the past …

Flying, floating again, high, high among clouds. "Parked up" in a lay-by. At last, at the *Italian* end of a great mountain tunnel! He has blinked at daylight, gasped at the view, patted Lotte's steering-wheel.

The Avro Anson! he mutters. Because now, he's looking at that lever in his floor by the door (through whose slot he can now see bright Alpine gravel). He made that plane once, as a model, and it made his Dad recall – he'd flown in an Anson the odd time, on air-gunnery practice or something – and said he remembered you had to pump a lever, literally pump at it, by hand and for quite a while, to get its unwieldy undercarriage down into landing position.

If Lotte's a flying machine in his mind, now she feels reborn, from that War before he was born, its "Phony" start-phase – as the Anson, with its slow pace, its panoramic set of windows, a plodding transport; not built for combat.

The Avro Anson, he thinks, yes; and now he pulls that floor-level lever to release, with a single clank, not Lotte's undercarriage, but the step that folds out below her door. Perhaps he should check his straps, his parachute …

The Avro Anson. Those Airfix kits. All those Spitfires, Hurricanes, Lancasters, Halifaxes and even, at last, the Short Sunderland Flying Boat – at 12s 6d the biggest and most expensive of all the kits – the "Flying Porcupine" (before and after the war a mainstay of Imperial Airways, the Empire Flying Boat….) He remembers constructing them, all those kits. Perhaps a hundred in the end. Alone, absorbed. At first, sticking fingers together more efficiently than the bits of aircraft. Painting them in their camouflage-patterns. All those decal-transfers to apply, denoting for instance the Bristol Blenheim or Douglas Boston as Allied forces; Junkers, Messerschmitt, Dornier – as Jerries. And oh, the store of useless knowledge – engine-types and bomb-loads, armament and Marks 2 and IIIA – he held in his brain back then; in the years before the same grey cells "grew up", supposedly, and started collecting quotations from literature instead.

But why – in the 1960s, his early teens, when already jet-powered nuclear V-Bombers were thundering overhead to deter another, Colder, foe – why, back then, did he want to do *that*? Why? Why, to get his Dad – his quiet, sometimes sad-seeming father, whose cartoonist/gunner-veteran's eyesight and hardware business career were starting to fail simultaneously – to talk. Not of course to help *him*. Just viscerally wanting him, unlike all other dads of his generation, to *talk* about – things.

But he – his dad – always seemed to think he was at risk of lapsing into two different sorts of disastrously-bad parental behaviour:

One: would be to "glorify", in some way, a war in which he'd flown in a plane that dropped bombs intentionally on German and Italian soldiers, incidentally also on some Italian civilians, maybe women and children, and certainly once according to the log-book – well, at least once – on his own troop positions in error. And so he wouldn't want any of his children glorifying war by glorifying him – in the case of that son, in those days, probably a reasonable fear – for 'fighting' in it.

Often when they went out and played at the park, and sometimes in the primary school yard, like many English boys then, he and his primary school friends would vary their 'Cavalry and Patchees' with 'English and Germans'. And kids' comics like the 'Victor' always made the dorsal gunner on an RAF medium bomber into a square-jawed sharpshooter. Whereas *he* would have known, it was unbelievably-difficult to hit anything with the curving line of tracer from your swivelling turret. Consequently, as gunner, you were shitting yourself when you spotted an enemy fighter, just as you were at another time when the anti-aircraft battery below began to get your range... So it would be bad, very bad indeed, to encourage the boy, by telling him anything about that war which might make him think his dad, or any of his dad's mates, had been a hero; or that fighting another, future war might in any way be exciting good fun. Discretion about war-service was always the better part of Cyril's valour.

Another bad thing his father felt he might do, would be Spoil, Ruin a boy: by giving him too much attention of *any* sort, especially a ten-year-old who seemed quite unreasonably to *want* it all the time. Give him too much Attention, and obviously he'd turn into a self-regarding Exhibitionist, that unbearable beast who in ordinary society would be shunned as Too Big For His Boots.

The Captain does understand that, now – and must in turn passionately hope he avoided the excesses both of Attention – and of seemingly-careless Ignoring – with his own kids. He actually "understood" even back then, that his dad was just *being how grown-ups were.* It was his way of training a boy to take a proper, modest, reticent place in the scale of things.

But like all young animals, this boy who knew no better, knew that he needed More. Though it was difficult, he'd try a trick sometimes, with a model plane accidentally left where it might be noticed. Or he'd pick up on and question some curious old turn of phrase which was only his dad's:

like "toes pointed like a tent-peg". By doing this he learned a worse-than-graphic expression used by a group of young airmen about the point when you might go vertically downward with your stricken, smoke-trailing aircraft, too low, too late, too on fire, too twisting through the air to make any use of a parachute … Simultaneously he would learn that this brutally-facetious set of words could be used by analogy in peacetime, to refer to the moment of knowing that all – in a failing business, say, or long illness – was lost, and known to be lost: a wry observation of instinctive, useless, blind, preparatory terror. *Toes pointed like a tent-peg.*

All the boy's finished model planes had been gathered in one newspaper-lined, dark bureau-desk drawer in the living-room, the second drawer down. This was under a drawer of his dad's, housing cartridge-paper, rolled drawings, pens, ink, pencils, all rather chaotic; which was itself below his parents' desk-top whose sloping lid opened onto the sliding chaos of envelopes, loose bills, old letters, insurance-policies and payment-books – their eternal, unmentionable, unforgiving, insolvent, financial Black Hole. (So many things – not just The War – were unmentionable in that family; and money was certainly one of them. There was hardly any.) From his own long, deep, reserved second drawer down below, he'd bring out: Heinkel, Zero, Focke-Wulf, Mustang. Hold them up against the light, squint to make them fly.

Or like a chess-piece move, not too ostentatiously, start to build a latest purchase: a Lockheed Hudson, or Messerschmitt 262 – while his dad was about – in the hope of a glance, some notice, some comment. With the Anson then, success!

Or sometimes, alone, stare in through the plastic "Perspex" cockpit-hood or turret at those stiff grey little air-gunners, their hands bonded together as if in prayer, stuck to the block-box on the back of that wobbly pair of black guns. He'd peer through plastic smear to see if he could make out an expression on that little feller's face. More than anything, though, he'd be trying to see out the other side, *through his eyes.* Through real, vibrating glass and riveted frame, the mad, shaking little greenhouse round helmet-head-phoned ears, scan the sky there for Macchi or Messerschmitt fighters. Jump when a flak-shell went off too near, leaving raw, roaring holes in wing and fuselage, maybe hurting the navigator. The boy kept trying to get his head inside that turret. And then try to imagine how, if you had to, you'd get out…

The shock-absorber clunks again, as he gets back out on the road down into Italy. Down, down, through clear vistas of morning. Glorious light on carved and polished, swooping high green valleys. Down, down into springtime Italy.

And now it's with a sense of once again laying bare a willed stupidity (in turning the wrong way onto the *Tangentiale* outside Torino – it's probably just exasperated tiredness) that the Captain pulls off at a *Servizio*. Muttering that this really *is* now all about his dad, he selects gear P for Park, hoists the handbrake, turns off Lotte's marvellous motor – and once again lights gas under his kettle.

Yes – pilots. Here *he* is, he's just 'flown solo', again, into Italy, something the old feller never did, in car or plane. Always the watchful air-crew, same as his other two mates, he hadn't been the pilot.

Admired pilots, though: Bob Connell. One of 223 Squadron's Australians, and the man his crew depended upon, rightly as it turned out, to get all four of them back safe, after missions whether successful, cocked-up or aborted en-route. The man whose nerve and expertise all of Cyril's four children, now aging, have to thank for their opportunity to be conceived – Yes, he mutters, thanks again, Bob, for bringing the Old Man back to hearth and home. And Dad'd be glad to have you here again with him.

What had Dennis Baker, also an air-gunner in 223 Squadron, said?[1] "We all had a lot of respect for our skippers …"

And the plane. Over time the twin-engined American-built A-23 Martin Baltimore "light bomber" would gain a decent, if low-profile, reputation for its war-record. It was much faster and more manoeuvrable than the Bristol Blenheim it replaced out in the Desert. But it really wasn't at all easy to take-off and land, and there were plenty of initial accidents.

It was a sister aircraft of the USAF's B26 Martin Marauder (a.k.a. "the Widowmaker") which was responsible, among new Allied aircraft made during that War, for a very serious number of *accidental* deaths to aircrew. It was notoriously a fact that a Marauder with one engine stalled was very hard indeed to keep in the air (and even tougher to land).

There were always, one might expect, going to be problems with such aircraft, too-rapidly developed during a war, and especially when flown by inexperienced pilots – but if you also throw in the profit-motive of what

---

[1]   Dennis Baker, in his nineties, in a chat on the phone from his Home Counties home

were large British[2], and much larger US, companies, you're in the territory of Arthur Miller's "All My Sons"[3], not to mention Joseph Heller's "Catch-22". Teething troubles would only be dealt with (in later "Marks" of the various aircraft) after the record of problems (crashes, deaths) encountered for the first time during combat missions began to accumulate.

Effectively, all new World War II planes were prototypes flown by novices. And Cyril may well have quietly hero-worshipped his pilot, Flt. Sgt. Bob Connell. Tall, sandy-haired, long-faced but grinning broadly in those old flying-crew photographs, his crew would have to place themselves, over and over, in his big Aussie hands and believe he'd get them back, whether struggling to fly level as the bombs were released through a shrieking, exploding sky, or whether some all-too-foreseen circumstance had them limping back. For instance, less than three weeks after their crash – and having apparently been grounded for a fortnight, for surviving that top-brass cock-up:

Ops8 as briefed Solimans L.G[4]. 16 of 223 & 2 other formations, escort several
squadrons. A/a v. concentrated. S/bd motor cut over target.
Came home alone at low level, evading light a/a & m.g. fire.

Well done, Skip.

Thanks, Bob.

No worries, mate.

They were always in broad daylight, always exposed.

---

[2]   In Britain, too, though such issues were (and still are) less talked about, even famed and feted aircraft like the Handley Page Halifax demonstrated serious operational weaknesses "Sqdrn Ldr. Leonard] Cheshire was amongst the first to note there was very low return rate of Halifax bombers on three engines; furthermore, there were reports the Halifax was unstable in a "corkscrew" which was the manoeuvre used by bomber pilots to escape night fighters. The fault was in the Halifax's rudder design and Cheshire became enraged when *Handley Page at first declined to make modifications so as not to disrupt production.*" Source: Wikipedia, citing: Hastings, Sir Max. Bomber Command (Pan Military Classics) London: Pan Books, 2010..[author's italics]

[3]   It was Glenn Martin, head of the US's Martin aircraft company, appearing in 1942 at a Senate Committee-hearing chaired by later-to-be President Harry S. Truman, who admitted that the Marauder was having problems because "the wings were too short" ... But, anyway, he shrugged, the contract was long agreed – they were too far down the line now. Only when Truman suggested that the contract might be cancelled, did Martin finally agree to do something to make the Marauder a little more "airworthy".

[4]   LG = Landing Ground; in this case an enemy airstrip

A damaged Baltimore over Tunisia, 1943. [historyofwar.org]

The daylight-bomber crewman – Jack, Cliff, Cyril, whoever – over North Africa, Sicily, southern Italy, was in some ways just ancillary cargo among the high-explosives, each of them always a nervous passenger aboard something over which he could exercise no real control. Control was Bob's. All the other three could do up there was be as watchful as possible over collective self-preservation, and repose their troubled trust (necessarily cranked up close to hero-worship) in a pilot who was in fact no more experienced in his job than they were in theirs.

Here's one of Steinbeck's successors as Great American Novelist, Joseph Heller, expanding on that reality – not as Catch-22's Yossarian, but heartfelt, as himself, in his old age's autobiography:[5]

> In December 1944 I was twenty-one and a half, and it is hard now, it boggles the mind now, to believe that a young kid like Ritter, whom I'd known the longest and who was somewhat stumpy in physique, was ever, let alone routinely as an occupational specialty, permitted to fly as a pilot at the controls of a twin-engined Mitchell medium-sized bomber that carried a bomb load of four thousand pounds (eight five-hundred pounders or four of a thousand pounds each) and five other human beings!

---

[5]   'Now and Then – an autobiography' Simon and Schuster 2004

How in hell did he learn to do that?

I, who didn't apply for my first driving license until I was twenty-eight, find it difficult to envision even now that a kind and unaggressive boy, so young, could learn to fly a bomber …

So, thinks the Captain: Bob Connell: Respect. A man he's sure his father, in retrospect, would have liked to be. The Man. And Bob was only – what? – 23 back then. Cyril was 27.

Now he remembers how, much later, twelve years or so after the war – he would have been about six – in the mid 1950s, his father learned for the first time to drive a motor vehicle. It was the first time he could have afforded one, and anyway it was "for the shop" – because by this time, Grandad Tom had retired from hardware and ironmongery, and Cyril had decided he needed to drive a small van, so that he could develop the business by delivering paraffin door-to-door.

And look! Hey, even a little boy could sense, there was a new swing to his walk. Now that Dad had passed the Test, he was getting out of *the pilot's seat*.

So after that, almost every Sunday afternoon, Cyril took his family out into the North Riding countryside. 1959, let's say, and five or six of them crammed inside the tinny little old van that stank of paraffin – to pick billycans of blackberries or bilberries, or ("for Grandma") bunches of wild primroses. Inside the case of that rusty little old 1948 Morris van, in the back, Sid would sit on one wheel-arch, Ros on the other (they'd hold onto metal struts between roof and wall) and he'd be perched on a slithering sea-grass stool in the middle of the floor behind the parents' seats. Brian the little brother would be in front, a babe or toddler in Mum's arms in front alongside the driver – long, of course, before any provision of seatbelts.

Health And Safety?

Oh, and behind all of them in the back, a smelly five-gallon drum of Pink Paraffin ready for delivery before opening the shop the next day.… and Dad of course smoking a fag as he drove.…. There, if ever there was one, should be the excuse for nightmares about a Burst Of Flame! But all was perfectly cosy and normal. There were never crashes or explosions. He always got everyone back. He had a reputation for being a very careful driver. Safe. Mission accomplished. No casualties in the crew.

Now, the Captain smiles, he's inherited an elbows-out, fingers-slightly-fisted walk. He's jumped down onto the ground at the *servizio* to make for the sandwich-bar and toilets, and – if that *is* something of his father's late-learned strut – then he senses that it's *also* partly the stride of a tall Australian Second World War bomber pilot.

The Man.

Chapter 13

*Lago d'Iseo – the Zen of campervanning – the company & singularity –
authenticity? – Romanino*

He considers, now that he's stopped here by his favourite Italian lake: there
are a number of activities, on campsite or at home, which it's easy to dismiss
as necessary-but-irritating housework. We get up in the morning, have a
shower, make coffee, make the bed, eat breakfast, wash up – maybe not all
of those things every morning, but if not some of them will be waiting for us
later when, no doubt, we return from work, or whatever else (always more
important) we've been doing. They're things done more or less in a state of
distraction, often of rush. They're generally necessary tasks – and for that
reason often irritating. They are, in our workaday lives, distractions, eaters
of what we think of as useful time; and of resources like water-heating and
foodstuffs which also have had to be bought with our limited labour, time
and cash. Most days very few of us seem to expect actively to *enjoy* what
has become a dazed ritual of getting self and family ready for the day, an
important day which we're already rehearsing as the subtext of brushing
teeth or gulping muesli. We don't pay much attention as we multi-task.

Now – observe Captain Kamper at Lago d'Iseo. The Zen of Camper-
vanning. He rises (or rather lowers himself with a gentle grunt) from his
bench-seat bed, reaches for the kettle without taking another step, lights his
gas and sniffs the faintly-sweet fume of gas-hob (and of heater, which he now
makes rumble by his feet). He dresses quickly, steps outside, casts his sight
around and walks briskly to relieve himself at the toilet-block. Returning, he
climbs back in, opens his high cupboard for a mug, his little fridge for milk
and his resealed packet of favourite coffee. He may not smell too savoury
himself right now, he reflects, peering out of the windows above the kettle at

a watchful, late-breakfasting rabbit on the grass; but no-one's complaining, or needing to suffer in silence. He adds water to the coffee. Now *there's* an odour to be savoured. He's free to sit down with the coffee-pot and peer out of another window at a different scene: a bit of a hedge, a swan on the lake, a gate, a path across another field, another gate, and at the top of a rise, some wind-carved trees, a mountain-ridge. He may sit over his coffee for a while, or stroll back outside with it. Maybe he reads yesterday's newspaper. Maybe he writes something in his journal. He considers his world. He puts the kettle on again for a second cup. He takes satisfaction even out of taking out the matches, striking, lighting, putting the matches away again; and from roughly swilling the little cafetiere to make a second mugful, from taking out again and putting away again the packet of coffee. Used matchsticks are dropped into the little rubbish carrier-bag that hangs between the cooker and the door. Everything was hidden and must come out of hiding. Everything that comes out, goes back away. There's little enough of anything and yet, under the surface, certainly enough of it, and he knows where it is.

On the surface, he's a man in a van. Underneath, he's a transporter and enjoyer of riches: his own, seemingly few enough and easily stowed; and of the world's, at his fingertips, all around him.

Washing up? He could do it in the van but he has paid a little to use the site's facilities, probably. The pots, a little sponge and the wash-liquid are put in the plastic washbowl. The tea-cloth goes over his arm. He strolls off to the sinks like a waiter in a Sunday afternoon beer garden. Bonjorno, he says to the lady returning from the other end of the block, a quilted cagoule over her pyjamas. Good morning, she says. (Silly man might as well speak English, she thinks.) He washes up. Each washing up is different, because he is paying attention and enjoying it. He spreads himself and his stuff out, and recollects it and himself again using the bowl; returns to the van and puts everything away, closes the cupboards. Now he opens another and pulls out his towel, washing things and sometimes a razor. He picks out clean underwear and socks, wraps them with the shower gel in the towel, and strolls down the same route to the showers. Here, again, there will be someone else's hot water which feels like nature's bounty this morning – and which is no doubt more economic than heating a whole water system just for himself.

His shower'll be one of at least forty in this bath-house this morning. If this is his first morning in a place, he will work out the variation which is provided upon the usual economy of hooks, shelves, shower controls and pressures in the bath-house. He'll decide whether it measures up to the last place, and to his preferences – this will help him to decide how long he stays. He stands under the water, so long as it's hot enough, for a good long time. He thinks thoughts. He towels dry and dresses, returns across the park letting the wind have a second go, after his quick towelling, at drying what's left of his hair. Back at the van he either lays the towel outside it, on the wing-mirror, or inside over the heater, depending on season and weather. Everything else goes away in the right place: used clothes in a plastic bag in a cupboard for washing at the end of the week.

Already he's having a day. A good day. These are the basic starting tasks of life and he's had time to savour them like a big breakfast. The endorphins are on form. He got up at about 7.30. It's now 9.

Maybe it's in something like this hope of emptied bliss we all go off on holidays: a hope of liberation not only temporary but somehow systemic. Certainly it's for this that this Captain feels he must sometimes escape to mountains, desert, sky, water.

And often – oh, he's so sorry – yes, for much of his time away in the van he *is* alone.

Lao d'Iseo. This is so often the forgotten Italian lake, smaller than, and between, the two memorable ones. A couple of years ago he decided he liked it here; and always knew it had to be on his route again this time: a detour for peace of mind. To take stock. The cool lake, the looming ridges beneath mountains, the swans, the camping village's undercurrent of chatter and radio-noise, the rich smell of cooking meats and sauces in the evenings. The town, within a short walk.

Look, under these crowded bird-loud trees by the lake, here are all types of campers, German, French, Dutch, Swiss, Italian: in small tents beside hatchback cars; in a bijou yellow Japanese four-by-four; in a little old grey Dormobile with a roof that opens like an accordion-bellows; in towed, single- or double-axle caravans; and in the 'static' rented vans that create the permanent central "village" of the site, with window-boxes, and even gnomes and wooden trellis. This time, there's actually one motorhome here just like his, except it has Einstein's portrait stencilled on the back, and the quotation (in German) that "The true sign of intelligence is not knowledge but imagination" – and the driver's a little white-haired Swiss man who even looks a little like his hero. He and the Captain disagree good-naturedly about whose van is older, then shrug and chuckle, patting one another.

All these vehicles of course have one thing in common. They contain a plurality of people. All except his.

Some of these folk, in caravans and larger camper-vans, are the pan-European camping couple of a certain age. Others, in smaller vehicles, or tents, are young couples either simply *a deux* or with one or two little children – ah, see that tiny, swaddled, white-capped baby! Or they arrive, still others, as whole extended families of up to six, at weekends, and colonise their static shanties; three chattering, shouting Italian generations will be represented. Even those two muscular young German women on their bicycles with their small tent, they're obviously together. And so much the better.

They're all pursuing a delightful seasonal dimension of their life: in family, in relationship and in society, and very delightful they find this shift of it all into the open air, under the trees, beside the lake, near to the town but just enough outside of it. Here they're all out in the open, and they lose their inhibitions – well, a little, some do, if they had a few before.

See – the dumpy blue-rinsed Belgian lady sits in her white towelling dressing-gown outside their newish Dethleffs van as if within her boudoir, while her tall grey husband, stripped to the waist, his torso wrinkled, sagging and not yet at all tanned, troops openly off to the toilet-block carrying a fat, pink bog-roll. They'd never behave like this, innocent as it is, in front of the neighbours at home! That young mother in the red bikini, carrying her toddler, is making her way to the open, grassy lakeside to sunbathe. As she might do on a crowded beach, perhaps. But here – ha! – she's ducking and sidestepping loaded washing-lines of other people's underwear! And the little group of rented 'statics': they may look like a little shanty-town, but their occupants, too, are *camping*. It's not at all the way they'd risk trying to live at home. It's a change, of course. Perhaps, generationally, it's nostalgia. It's a change, it's a rest. And thus it's the essence of holiday, together.

Now it can't be said that the Captain's appearance here doesn't in itself run along the wheel-tracks of campsite-normal. He, too, is often to be seen in unflattering, long, pocketed shorts, and dries his laundry on Lotte's bike-rack and side-mirror-bars. But there's that one aspect that others always, he feels, notice in him as strange. Yes: he appears, in that van, to be alone.

He feels that – floating its unspoken question – around him, in an occasional glance from out of this polyglot village. What is the solitary man in the old Hymer there for? What is he doing, surrounded by people with whom out of language-mismatch he can barely do more than exchange a greeting? In his mind, it isn't only here of course, but arriving at every continental site really, on this trip: whether just overnight or for a few days. The *patron* has leaned across the desk – "one camping-car, *e persone due*? Oh – one only. Excuse me. *Uno.*" Noted correctly in the column. Like the Captain's father. Keeping the Log correct, and much unsaid.

He's pretty sure he's the only English camper here today. And mostly, he must hope that the other campers'll just put his oddness down to nationality. He smiles and exchanges greetings and continues to practice his small stock of Italian phrases. He does a lot of walking, he shops in town. There's a wonderful *gelateria* there, by the lake-side. He doesn't seek out conviviality and colloquy though, and it feels that the less he has of that, the less he wants it. His stomach for socialising, never great, can actually shrink on this diet.

But it's all for the best. For the moment the Captain's got tired of driving, already tired of *Autorotes* and *Tangentiales*. And since he's decided he'll stay here for a few days, he does feel a number of changes, internally. He's escaped from a sense of being pursued, and feels that he can now afford to be *in pursuit* of something.

What have pursued him are questions of childhood, younger manhood, history, responsibility. Here at least he starts to feel he's shaking them down. And he's shrugging off an identity of "should" and "ought" – except occasionally (if only for his own sense of rightness) he "should" have a shower. Now, he's examining the sense of what will be "being Dad all over again" at the wedding. In what ways might this be a bad – and in what ways a good – thing?

And he's reading Charles Taylor, the Canadian thinker, who in his "Ethics of Authenticity" makes a very strong case against life lived as the atomised individual. Personal self-determination, he argues, is *not* about hermetic absorption. It must take place "against the horizon" of the world – of our origins, of our relationships, of society.

That's right, thinks the Captain. Spot on. At the same time the individual who has been too much "in the world" – at times unable to see wood for all the interactive trees – must sometimes find insights into his impulses and habits of feeling, in solitude. This, by the lake at Pisogne, is neither absolute good in itself, nor apathetic escape into solipsism.

Lago d'Iseo, this sliver of mirror-glass in a V of mountains, does pretty well as Taylor's horizon for now. Its reflective, winking surface provides not the social, relational mirror of the world that is sometimes too much with us, so much as a curved lens into Through-The-Looking-Glass paradox. He may be "alone". At the same time he's *chosen to be in the midst* of a multifarious, quizzical company of others. Clearly he wants to be "in the world" as well. He's allowing himself to be in this world, even if he's not *of* it. From the present, to consider the past, and the future.

In the mirror of the lake too, his own face and his father's swim first into one, then back to separate portraits.

On his walks, he's been drawn in afresh by the remarkable frescoes in the Chiesa di Santa Maria della Neve, in town. By Romanino, these biblical figures (even the Fra Angelico-inspired Angel in the Annuciation) carry huge, peasant strength – even a fulsome fleshiness – that makes Jesus positively curvaceous as he levitates into heaven, demonstrating all the laidback aplomb of a circus-trapeziste, winched up on her swing.

Up there in the ceiling on all sides among God's arches, prophets mingle with cherubs beside curving pillars, and have been painted ingeniously with shadows thrown behind them, as if they are actually, physically, hanging onto the girders of the big-top themselves – or, in the case of the cherubs, have become tumbling, free-floating statues.

Are their toes pointed? Of course not. They even levitate him into their sphere.

A paradox:

To look properly at the past, he needs to rise above it.

To rise above, he needs to look at it properly.

Anyway this place is real, Captain, and you're here.

Back at the campsite, a swan swings expertly in the current. Her children puff out their chests to keep up.

Di Luca Giarelli – Opera propria, CC BY-SA 3.0, https://commons.wikimedia.org/w/index.php?curid=4445863

Chapter 14

Memory, not Remembrance – Cyril post-War

Do elephants ever forget? Even crossing the Alps? What does he *need* to Remember?

Last time he was in Italy, none of this actually preoccupied him at all. Pisa, Florence, Milan, Verona, Venice … Standard tourist places soon to be crossed-off as seen. And he wasn't alone. Often, enough pressure, excitement and adventure, just in seeking out places to stop in the van; staging-posts on hillside or lagoon-edge….

He already expects, as he travels much further south, there will still be many days when that sort of site-spotting activity – and negotiating the E-ways, those Italian *autostrada* motorways he remembers from previous visits, permanently lined with cones and road-works, all bumping, vibrating, ribbed asphalt-slabs under his hard German wheels – will be all that there is to attend to. What he needs to remember will stick.

But his dad, that war: as the Captain heads south, is he attempting Remembrance? No, that's just more pompous, and less focused, than looking at the actual record, at his own research and *just remembering* – even though he often catches himself trying to forget, or reconstruct.

On "Remembrance", too – that bronze or marble, reconstructed word – their father trained them all by judicious, unspoken "No comment". Once a year the young family might find themselves watching on telly the petals falling "on the massed ranks of all the Forces", as Raymond Baxter intoned sententiously over a "Festival Of Remembrance" at the Albert Hall or wherever. But they'd probably only be watching because, in 1960s and 70s public broadcasting, there was "…nowt else on tonight." And Cyril'd be off to the pub halfway through, 9.40 pm, exactly the same as any other night. Certainly, he'd never be seen to shed or blink back a tear over Remembrance. (Question: Is it the case that on-screen, becoming unable to speak halfway through a sentence, giving way to its emotion, is entirely our updated, learned habit for the public media? Cyril, you see, would have distrusted first its authenticity, then its propriety, then its cliché.)

He never claimed, as one Grammar-school teacher once memorably did to a rebellious class, "I fought and died for the likes of you". Unspoken, remained: the fact that from a war, it's lucky to return unscathed – and unchanged, impossible. Of course, they always wore their poppies in November – normally, like most people then, just on the day – but Cyril's children never learned to glorify the conflict, or the "sacrifice" of the "fallen". In fact it had been for entirely-opposite purposes that this son had so obsessively recreated it in Airfix, 1:72 scale...

Cyril would always front up, any time, as cheerful. He was popular with (particularly the old) ladies, and carried himself with a little man's swagger. He would always be kind and generous to others. Under the barrage of his wife's impatience that nothing in the family's circumstances ever really changed or improved, he would become wistfully, fatalistically exasperated: "Whoever told you that life was *fair*?"

After that, and rarely, his most emphatic statement under serious assumed-attack was wearily to "go out for a walk", in town, which otherwise would not have been his habit at all. In fact, in all things he was mightily habitual. Maybe most men of his time were. Was it their means of controlling, without having openly to dictate?

Admittedly, the life of his community, in those days before flexible hours and working from home, was very highly-structured. It suited. Monday to Saturday (early-closing-"half"-day, Wednesday) you could set your watch by his hours of work, in first his own, later a new boss's hardware shop. On Saturday afternoons when his own dad, Granddad Tom, was still alive, Cyril would leave the old shop to him and take his second son to watch the town's non-League football team. There, he would stand in a corrugated-iron covered stand without seats with a group of men his own age and older, in belted gabardines and trilby hats. His little boy was given a rickety pile of bricks to wobble on, twenty feet away, right at the front, clinging to the top of the flaking white picket-fence and right in the stink of wintergreen and steaming mud, praying for their team's mad winger to do his trick. His dad's cadre of men would pride itself that it didn't shout, but would watch the match in quiet, conversational judgement both of the team and of a younger chap standing nearby called Doug, who wanted to join that group but who (apparently to gain their notice) was embarrassingly-loud. Cyril wasn't the leader of the group – that was a tall, long-chinned man called Edgar – but he was a comfortable lieutenant.

In those days when men could smoke when and where they wanted, this dad smoked quite heavily, maybe thirty to forty Bristol a day. And in those days, too, when drinking was done exclusively in the pub, and pubs were dark, exciting places out of which children and respectable women could only savour excluded, walking by doorways, the mingled smells of smoke, beer, urine – concentration and amplification of the odour, in those days, of men in general – he used to drive off to the pub at 9.40pm every night and would seldom have drunk less than three pints of bitter before leaving time at 10.30.

The Captain reckons he'd already be dead if he'd ever approached anywhere near this scale of habit-adherence. (Still, he does like a beer himself, and continues to smoke the odd Benson or three.) His dad wasn't extraordinary in smoking and drinking his way. It was the social norm for most men. Perhaps the drinking, at least, still is for many.

Other habits: once a week, into this son's teens, he was out in uniform to the local ATC "squadron" which he led as "Squadron Leader"; and once a month, to the Forty Club, the local (men's) debating society. Twice a year at best, he'd attend the Methodist Chapel and take his second wife Mildred with him. He would be immaculately dapper, and sing an improvised sort-of-descant tenor, which women in particular again admired; she, on the other hand, would have agonised over this social ordeal of formal going-out. In order it seemed perversely to intensify her torture, she'd never bring herself (out of some obstinate but obscure principle, or on the grounds that 'they didn't fit') to wear a hat or gloves – so making herself feel even more that she "stood out".

In most of his public habits Cyril wasn't exceptional in his time and place. But what was certainly more unusual was his use of time at home before the pub, between say, 7pm and 9, especially on weekdays. If the high-school children had done all their homework, the way the family became a family – other than at meal times, or while watching Z Cars together on Wednesdays – was over games. Subbuteo table-football – Dad against the boys? Why not? Cards, with all five or six, including Mum, round the table: rummy, knock-out whist, "Solo"? Scrabble, with one or two junior opponents? OK.

Big, packaged, marketed board-games, he wasn't so keen on – but the sons and daughter were allowed to feel modern, as the youngest got older, with such as Monopoly, Totopoly, Secret Agent, Formula One. Certainly, he taught his family to enjoy *playing* – and then, to learn to deal with the embarrassing frustrations of losing, by cultivating facetious impersonations of despair: it was important not to be seen "*taking it too seriously*".

Later, on his return from the Vic (the Victoria Hotel – he never called it "the pub") – younger children long abed, older ones expected to take themselves off or to keep quiet, there was for him, up to and around midnight, a little quiet time. He might sit, smoke and read a library book (Lord Peter Wimsey, Berry and Co, Wodehouse, Damon Runyon) while his wife darned, sewed, knitted, or read the latest family saga by R.F Delderfield; then she'd head upstairs herself.

Then finally, late-sitting, he might sit at the table and sketch, expertly, little "types" of cartoonish chaps. In the top bureau-drawer (beneath the gloomy desk-top of bills, and above his middle son's Selected Aircraft Of World War Two In Plastic) was Cyril's drawer containing, among other detritus, A2 cartridge-paper sheets of rather expert drawing exercises from a correspondence course he'd taken some years before. There they remained after his death, having never been worked up beyond that. He'd also done landscapes, local rural scenes, on 'scraperboard', in which he quietly took some pride. For a couple of years, the local paper published his black-and-white artworks and weekly "pocket cartoons" – local and topical jokes, sporting asides and silly puns.

"My dear, mine eats like a horse!"

Still, somewhere along the line he'd given that all up; even though it would be a few years yet before his eyesight started to fail significantly. It wasn't going to pay, or to be of *practical* use. Therefore, not to be indulged.

And it's extraordinary, he thinks. The old man was what nowadays, let alone *then*, would probably be accounted very much a "hands-on" father in his family. How then can the Captain *still* feel that he's working off obscure clues about *who* this father was? The fact is he finds he inherited a shell to inhabit, a shadow to imitate. Cyril's watchwords were "toleration" and "consideration" – for others. But who was *he*? Even at full throttle and at play, what his family mainly learned from him was to be increasingly-expert at hiding their cards, at making jokes from behind them, and at making the best of things even when exasperated beyond measure, perhaps at times even to despair.

At the same time, four children, of two different mothers (Muriel, the first, by then deceased and – worse – never mentioned, except occasionally, rebelliously, by Mildred, the second – but then *she* had a long-absent dead father, also unspeakable) they all, to the quiet satisfaction of their parents at least, became "successful" adults, one way or another. It must have been much, much more difficult for his older brother and sister. Circumstances had actually extended "The War" into that period of Cyril's life: *all* off-limits. Silent censorship. Times that lay just before that third child's birth became a multi-dimensional void: a recent past they all were wordlessly forbidden to visit.

Don't mention the War! And not just that.

Perhaps the Old Man did share stories, and personal loss, in the Vic or the Alma, with one or two ex-Service pals – long-chinned Edgar, for one. They'd have been the only ones, he might have felt, to understand however non-verbally what it meant: following orders; military 'Duty' as a column of a balance-sheet; depersonalised separation from wife and family, and from questions of morality and free-will; nightmare; repressed panic; preservation of self; powerlessness to preserve others. Abeyance therefore of the very values and freedoms they were told they fought for. But what's new? That's war.

As to the loss of friends and loved ones… once it was known about, it would have been agreed it was best not talked about.

Least said soonest mended.

Hard lines.

Anything for a quiet life.

Now, he remembers Cyril as always completely-automatic in his efforts to help anyone out, to find an answer to another's worry, to prevent potential disaster or possible discord: and so in company, in family, in relationship, it would become always the Captain's "own" nature to try to spot needs even before they were expressed. In his teens at football he was always the goalie, placed in position to Save the team. Perhaps he liked the drama, but it was mainly about anticipating; predicting the run of the play; second-guessing. Crouching, peering, dancing tip-toe sideways on the line – out a little – then back, glancing for his posts – then pointing, shouting, warning. On pins.

With luck, Saving. In other words, permanently-anxious.

He piggy-backed his own numerous nameless childhood anxieties, later, onto Cyril's ever-willing formulation of the *fatherly* role. For instance: mentally, to wake at 4 a.m., to have the car ready and loaded to run for the hills with the kids, at the first sign of nuclear mobilisations.

He thinks he's always been pursued by a liver-pecking bird of obedience to duty-to-foresee, prevent, protect. But now, here at least, he can sit on his *own* high rock, and not the one the old gods would like to have him strapped to. He felt that vulture fall off Lotte's roof with a scrape of talons, somewhere just past Milan. He knows it may try to flop back aboard at any time. Maybe, heaven forefend, may perch on his shoulder as he heads for the wedding – or for home afterwards. Part of the Quest therefore in this game of ancestors and archetypes must be for some crackerjack or potent charm with which *permanently* to dispel the claws on the back, the sharp beak in the gut. He must cast more generously that habitually-averted eye of his – a blankness that defensively discourages his own expressive contact for fear that he might embarrass; or worse, that something will hungrily again be *needed*. He must find, if not a Heaven to levitate into, at least a guiltless calm and a way to access it – if only for a few moments each day – and keep that up when he does get back home.

Only when they became adults themselves would Cyril's children receive a few leaks from a never-written war-memoir. In the end, the Captain would have heard three specific tales: a crash on take-off; a tailspin; a fighter on the tail. Leaks, is what they were.

By this time Cyril knew his whole life might be leaking, and was finding he didn't want at last to be an uncommunicative man entirely, once his children were themselves independent, rarely-seen adults…. Anyway, he might have believed ever since 1943 that he'd been living on borrowed time. Hence "the tape"; e.g.:

> " *...I don't know whether it affected many other fellows the same way, but it did strike me that, if I were to be killed at this time, I hoped it would be by enemy action. The longer the War lasted, the more this feeling hung over me that I should be very annoyed, indeed, if I got killed in some – stupid mishap or other – and St Peter would probably giggle when I reported in at the main gate, and might even pull my leg a little...*"

It's about 1980, and a 28-year-old pre-Captain, already promoting up his career-ladder and married with a first child of his own, is leaving the old local with his Dad.

There are the older men's usual parting shouts down the street:

"Tomorrow night then, Dennis."

"All bein' well." Of course this means, *God Willing.*

"Aye, all bein' well, lad."

And his Dad, on the way to the car he's about to drive, half-blind these days even *before* he's had a drink, turns to the young man. "Isn't it daft what grown men can't bring themselves to talk about?" He means, Death. For about a second, he holds blurry eye-contact, locating his car-keys in a deep pocket. "Same as some folk can't talk about masturbation."

The only time he's ever been heard to use the word. And ever will be.

Chapter 15

*Emilia Romagna & the Newbys – Bologna – Because We Can – Mussolini –
Zamboni – Morandi – rebellion/collusion – artists & schizoids*

The Captain reflects, not for the first time nor the last: there's a striking lack of anything very much, in English-language print, about the impact of World War 2 – upon Italy.

"Love and War in the Apennines", a memoir by Eric Newby, does inevitably get to it, and so do a couple of the better history books[1]; not forgetting "Catch-22" – such characters as "Nately's whore".

Newby: (as you'd expect – especially if you've read his wonderful travel books) basically comes out of this book as just a good, real man. Taken prisoner in 1942 in an abortive Special-Ops in Sicily – then later, with a broken ankle, released into chaos, at the time of the Italian "Armistice" – he lives wild – and with local peasants' self-endangering support – in hiding from the occupying Germans, high in the mountains of Emilia Romagna, for months – until the middle of Winter 1943.

Briefly, the tale: he's met Wanda, a Slovene-Italian girl on a bicycle. They fall in love, but have been separated by their helpers, for the safety of both. Finally, he is forced to make a long trek (his whereabouts having finally been compromised) to yet another hiding-place the Italian villagers have selflessly set up for him. In all this, stiff-upper-lipped in general, he doesn't say much that is fundamental about himself; except, on that long final trek:

---

[1]   James Holland: "Italy's Sorrow" – Harper Press 2008;
       Baldoli and Knapp: "Forgotten Blitzes"- Continuum Books 2012

"That night something happened to me on the mountain. The weight [of a sack of rice he was carrying] coupled with the awful cough which I had to try and repress broke something in me … part of my spirit went out of me, and in the whole of my life since that night it has never been the same again"

Especially considering that this book was first published in 1971, nearly thirty years after the events he's describing, that is quite a statement.

Anyway, after the War, Newby went back, sought out and reunited with the girl. They married and spent the rest of their lives together – well, except for some of his travelling to write, and writing to travel. Many loyal readers know that his humorous sense of humanity remained undiminished until his death in 2006, aged 87, survived by Wanda. Her own book, "Growing Up In Fascist Italy" is well worth reading too.[2]

The stories of escaped prisoners like Newby, helped by those good people, illuminate ordinary Italians' natural response to any other's injury and deprivation – even if the result might prove calamitous for the helpers, as so often it did at that time. Rooting for the underdog is encultured in more races than the British, and perhaps less preciously.

Last night, the Captain sent the Muse his love, by email. It was his first encounter with an opportunity (and perhaps with the impulse) other than by text-message, for a few days. Nowadays, we do things "because we can". He thinks: it's a modern catch-phrase, to do something "because I can". It's no better than 'Because I'm Worth It' or 'Just Do It' – catchphrases of breathtaking brainlessness and amorality, even by the standards of 21st Century advertising. Now, *that's* his dad talking – updated!

It's half-past eight in the morning, on the Bologna City campsite – a beautiful place of its kind, and an example to all cities everywhere. The day's heat is already beginning to build. The milk he bought two days ago has gone off now. Oh, but fortunately, there's some more in the fridge too, against this eventuality. There's nothing worse at his time of life than to have to consider shopping before coffee.

---

[2]   Eric Newby: "Love and War in the Appennines" paperback Harper Press 2010
Wanda Newby: "Peace & War – growing up in Fascist Italy" Collins 1991

And at this time of life, it's precisely 'because you can', that you do what you do. Not *while you still* can – that would be thinking negatively – but because you can, *for the first time*. You can! Now, you *can* just – go. You can send your love, and have it returned, by phone or email or text message or postcard (take your pick) but you don't have to take your Love along.

If he stayed at home with her (and she still wants to work, still enjoys it, and how much is that to be admired?) he'd only be underfoot. Here, he's underfoot only to the Philippino woman swabbing out the men's toilets, crazily, at just the busiest time in the morning.

Well, and if he stayed at home he'd sometimes even get under *his own* feet. So he's going because – and yes, it still feels fresh and new – because he can.

Remember, Captain, those shared lifts to work, twenty five years ago, with Trev and Mike? In Trev's big Datsun, the three of you'd get to that big roundabout (you were in Lancashire in those days) with its sign pointing to the motorway, and you'd all say – all three of you, *only about thirty years old, for God's sake* – in unison: "Blackpool today?" as Trev swung the wheel then, grinning grimly, ploughed the dutiful old furrow through the rain towards inner-city Manchester again instead. More facetiousness, see? Since then, it's taken more than twenty-five years to reach the point where, with the same sense of rebellious imagination, but at last also of achievement, he can say: "Florence, today?" Because now, he can. He repeats this notion to himself, often. And he'll be meeting up with dear old Mike, now a 'vanner too, in Florence tomorrow. That has a circularity that satisfies in itself.

The Captain looks around him, here in the building heat of a Bologna morning on a spotless campsite: and sees a solid rank, maybe twelve vehicles in all, the same stamp and size, nothing particularly showy, skippered mainly by men of his own age (but generally taller, more distinguished-looking, he always regrets) in sandals, long shorts and sober-hooped polo-shirts with horizontal narrow stripes. And the wives: in voluminous floral culottes, big sunglasses.

He looks at their faces and figures, and considers them. Their walking, sometimes with a small dog on a correct lead, will be slow and studied. Their bare legs still look (*always* will, maybe, now, at their age) somewhat unaccustomed to air, sun and scrutiny. They're quiet, watchful, and pursue a kind of decorum, whether or not they exhibit togetherness (some do, some don't). About a third of these people here at Bologna Municipal are English, dotted about the site. They don't club inseparably together here as the Germans or the Dutch seem to do.

And each in their own way, these people are quietly defiant. They look at themselves in the mirror or at one another (the same thing?) and smile a particular sort of smile. It says, "Now we can do this. If we could have done it earlier, we would have. But starting now means we'll appreciate it all the more. If we'd been able, magically, to do it then, instead of working and having a family – well, of course we'd have done it, but sourly: sourly as we might even be enduring the discomforts and limitations of camper-life now, if we hadn't already had enough of our old dreams of static home comforts".

They've realised, in time, these caravan couples, that they're turning into free molecules: little cells of optimistic white, or grey, or cream, decalled with yellow sun-disks and blue-wave stripes. This is the next challenge – and so, they're cruising the motorways and by-lanes of Europe – right now, as we speak or write, or read, or work – yes, any time of day or even night, any time of year. Tiny beetles on huge charts – cruising around German forests, Spanish mountains, French vineyards, Italian cities; free molecules, ions, you might say, cruising to combine eventually with some other substance in all this – or becoming stretched,

"like gold to airy thinness beat"

from home into Something Else?

The Captain won't be patronizing them or, among them, himself. Yes, they're all doing things because they can.

And, OK – while they can. He wants to believe that old-fashioned idea that years bring experience, and with that, wisdom; though he doesn't want to let that lead him to patronise the young – either of his own youth, or his own children's generation. How *they* deal with the world of *today*, at their age, is beyond him.

So – who's to say these people aren't also sometimes thinking tragic thoughts? A lot of them, like him from time to time, probably are. But the essence of tragedy isn't its newspaper-headline meaning: sad event. Tragedy is individual nobility fallen, inevitably, from the height of its powers – and no doubt in part by its own proud fault – into sudden, clear-sighted understanding of its individual scale; of the human being under the heavens; an insect on a map; of errors left to be fixed by younger, later generations.

It's half an hour's brisk walk from the campsite into the beautiful city centre. Bologna itself, ancient city and the site of the earliest university in Europe, in the post-War years would become the examplar of Italian Communist municipal rule. The city's character remains unique, its towers and churches appropriately russet-red. And here is the Piazza Nettuno, home of a very fancy fountain (by Giambolonga, *circa* 1560) featuring nymphs with squirting nipples.

Now in 1926, when *Il Duce*, Benito Amilcare Andrea Mussolini, processing in celebration, on the fourth anniversary of his "March on Rome", to open a new sports stadium, approached this very spot – a young anarchist, Anteo Zamboni, a mere fifteen years old, attempted to assassinate him. His shot missed, and he was immediately strung up by Fascist *squadristi*, who in their brutal work had no need of any recourse to law. (The Pope gave public thanks to God.) There are now two streets named after the poor lad, to the east of the city centre.

"Don't mention the War", said Basil Fawlty again in 1975. Nowadays in Italy, it's very easy not to mention it. Still, it must still be everywhere – as many things are, that are never mentioned.

Thus, whenever the creative work of any mid-twentieth-century male European artistic figure is critically considered – be he artist, musician or writer – political biography is brought suddenly to the fore. It is, thinks the Captain, as if some of us, minnows who swim along after these big fish, can only justify our opinions as regards their art and its "moral value" by asking such as Sartre, Britten, Grass, Auden, Camus, Matisse: "What did you do in the War, Daddy?" hoping perhaps that by discomfiting their memory we may pull them down closer to our level. In some cases, we'll be meanly successful.

À propos, in a plodding loop (it's getting hotter, as Italian spring noondays do) via these streets, the Captain visits the via Fondazza, stately byway and long-time home of a favourite artist, Giorgio Morandi, who died in 1964, and whose prime included the Fascist era. A significant figure in Bolognese and Italian art through the inter-war period and beyond, Morandi is now seen by some as having hovered rather too close to the Fascist art establishment[3]. Before, during and after the war, however, his art barely changed focus, and throughout his career there's no indication of any political sympathy or statement.

---

[3]   Janet Abramowicz "The Art of Silence" 2004 Yale University Press

That's unsurprising. Giorgio Morandi had already been to War once, back in 1915. He'd been invalided out with a physical and nervous breakdown. All his subsequent work, overwhelmingly in the form of paintings and etchings of *natura morta* (that telling Italian phrase: in English we say "still life") and landscape, doesn't ever quite escape a kind of staring shell-shock. It's obvious that Morandi resolved to steer pretty clear of any active involvement in politics – and "steering clear" is, you might say, itself a political position (*tacere est consentire*). Certainly he didn't try to emulate poor Zamboni. But his life under Mussolini's regime was no more complacent or co-operative than most other people's. Yes, he shrewdly became a member of the Party for a time, but he also courted trouble with the Fascists by retaining friendships and working connections with artists and others who were definitely not.

The Captain has probably been drawn to this particular artist's work because of its trademark characteristic: figurative as it is, this unassertive art presents an absolute absence of the human figure. And instead of depicting any sense of life, let alone heroic Futurist action, Morandi invests dust-laden bottles and other obscure shelved objects in their dusty atelier-atmospheres (and equally, a couple of exterior landscapes) with something like neurasthenic *rigor mortis* – a sense of suddenly being caught in the headlights? Or sometimes just a wry acknowledgement of the personal necessity to be still – and to be where, and what, one finds one is at the moment, animate or inanimate. The humanity of the pictures lies in the mind-states of the artist and his spectator, which move about in domesticity somewhere between hidden trauma, and gratitude for the safety from others that isolation brings. Often, as in a child's imaginative play, groups of bottles on a shelf begin almost to develop human characteristics, relationships, as you look. Maybe a story the child, to stay calm, might play out by himself.

For much of the time Morandi was a recluse. Perhaps the fact that he hasn't, until now, been a headline name in the Anglo-Saxon consciousness is because his work, uninhabited by the literal human form, portrays neither (say) Munch's expressionist screaming nor Hopper's blank bar-hawks and hotel-dwellers. (Maybe Hopper's series of remote lighthouses – which his wife bitterly described as his self-portraits! – come closest to the spirit of Morandi.)

The Captain, lately, has become more and more interested in his own solitary mind-states. He's always acutely aware of the thoughts and feelings, real and imagined, of others. But certainly, he can be a bit introspective at times. Is that better than worrying about the Bomb, or volcanoes, or...? Like Morandi, he enjoys his periods of solitude, even though that can cause a problem to those close to him.

In a world moving inexorably towards an expectation of infinite connectedness, the ability to become absorbed into one's own world can come to be frowned-upon – even "clinically" – as "schizoid", the term seeming to imply a condition bordering on psychosis: only a step away from schizophrenia itself. According to the eminent Winnicott, schizoid individuals

"prefer to make relationships on their own terms and not in terms of the impulses of other people."[4]

Oh? And? ...Another expert believes

"it is possible for schizoid individuals to form relationships with others based on intellectual, physical, familial, occupational, or recreational activities as long as these modes of relating do not require or force the need for emotional intimacy, which the affected individual will reject"[5].

---

[4]   D.W. Winnicott1965 *The Family and Individual Development* p.73

[5]   Ralph Klein, 1995 *Disorders of the Self: New Therapeutic Horizons*, Brunner/Mazel

This schizoid individual, multiplied by eleven, sounds like the personnel of most cricket teams the Captain has played for… One study regards it as a problem for 1% of the population; another, for 40% of inner-city males. It can only be comforting to him that the definitions are pretty broad, open to interpretation and dispute. Giorgio Morandi was perhaps more subject to this condition than most people; but then again many artists, writers, creative mathematicians, scientists and musicians would be.

And surely – solitariness of nature, unless with a socially-acceptable purpose, has always been demonised. A woman with this condition would for centuries past have been branded a witch. Quiet folk have always had to find something purposive, like carrying a fishing rod, or stroking a cat, as moral cover … But the solitary, the silent, the introspective, the observant – and the just plain thoughtful – among us may fail to provide a good excuse regularly enough. Perhaps, thinks the Captain, we should turn up to any vacuous "social" situation wearing a sandwich-board: "I may seem standoffish, cold, superior, odd – but you can comfort yourselves by calling me Schizoid".

Does this "diagnosis" then label the solitary, creative, exploratory work, of many writers, composers, musicians, artists of many sorts, as by definition ill, or even slightly mad, the Captain wonders? And if so, why do the conventionally-sane go to *their* artefacts for inspiration? He'll readily admit that by modern-day standards the behaviour of religious Stylites perched atop their poles – right across central southern Europe and into Russia, for a period of nearly ten centuries, well into the Middle Ages – now finally seems pretty bizarre. Then again, what about the worldwide admiration for round-the-world solo yachts-men and -women, for solitary polar explorers, for desert trekkers; and for philosophers like Wittgenstein?

The vast majority of schizoid individuals, it's asserted,

"show an enormous capacity for self-sufficiency and the ability to operate alone, independently and autonomously, in managing their worlds".

What a strange "disorder" that is! The Captain's left wondering to what extent clinical notions are determined by fashionable conventional consensus. For a new era of "connectedness" and hyper-communication, he suspects human society has started to define as "deviance" and "disorder", behaviours which have always been part of its broad, healthy spectrum.

Anyway, there's nothing the matter with *him*.

Under Fascism, the political choices for the quiet Mr Morandi were, as ever: involvement v isolation; rebellion v collusion. Key ethical questions of any time, but by now, curiously unimportant in the process of becoming enthralled by his art.

An artist of any kind may one day come to be seen as one of Shelley's "unacknowledged legislators of mankind". But they will often have had an actual distaste for legislation or moral generalisation of any sort. A concerned friend once pointed out to Giorgio Morandi, for instance, that his dealer was buying his work from him at a low price – and then selling it on in Rome and Milan at a multiplying factor of at least ten. Surely this was wrong? Was he not being exploited? Did it not make him angry?

"You don't understand. Let me explain something to you. I am an artist. He is a trader. These are completely different things."

Another story, the Captain likes even better. Late in his life, Morandi is living quietly in the rather-unprepossessing hill-village of Grizzana, fifteen miles outside Bologna. A local man buys a painting directly from the artist, and therefore not at a "trader's" price, to give to his daughter and her fiancé as a wedding present. When the time comes, however, the man changes his mind and buys the couple a silver-service instead. At length, tormented by guilty conscience, he confesses to the artist about this. "I am so sorry, Signor Morandi, but I liked your painting too much. I kept it for myself".

Morandi was so pleased with him, he gave him his money back.[6]

6   *Giorgio Morandi's Dust: documentary written and directed by Mario Chemello* 2009 [DVD] Bologna: Imago Orbis

Chapter 16

Bologna to Firenze – & bad-boy status – & on-time for rendezvous

Sixty miles south-east of Bologna, near Forli, is Mussolini's birthplace. There's a museum. Only recently, the local Commune (amid some contention both locally and nationally) finally banned the sale here of Fascist paraphernalia....

As he drives past Forli and onwards, he's starting to learn what will over weeks become a grindingly hard, hot lesson, even though they've been this far south before – already, Italy's going to be a large, long country for Lotte to drive all the way down. Mentally he's always made it smaller; and so much greater, the miracle of Ancient Rome's Mediterranean ascendancy. After all, unlike our own exceptional island-group, joined onto the mass of mainland Europe, Italy's always looked on English school maps like a little appendix off the European bowel.

What's more, in his head, he's always made it *flatter* than it is. Churchill and his generals had remembered it like that too, in their little atlases, before they took the invasion on in 1943... "The soft underbelly ..."

Such hills, such mountains! You do meet this kind of country early, coming down to Turin and Milan from the Alps. (Every schoolboy can tell you, the Alps are in France, Switzerland, Austria; try telling that to a Piedmontese).

Now, *en route* from brave Bologna to magnificent Firenze, thinking to be in the lowlands for a good long while, it's with a shock that he and Lotte meet this upward grind of winding, growling heavy goods vehicles on a road no better than a poorly-surfaced dual carriageway. Forever swerving into superannuated tunnels with dodgy lighting, worn lane-markings; into uphill, twisting tunnels after short deceptive flats and straights; a road that contrives to feel dark even on high ground on a hot day. And just now, when they've kidded themselves they really have got the revs to get past this gravel-truck on this incline –

No!

And now – welcome to our road! – they must endure the operatic horn-work which is the Italian drivers' (literal) *forte*, from one-to-twenty cars back, as he pulls back in – and they pass. They will now *each* tell him with an upturned palm through a downturned window, that they don't know what such a vehicle is doing on their road, and that he's now delayed them crucially in whatever journey they are intent upon today.

Certainly they can be a terrible nuisance on such roads, anywhere – campervans, caravanners – he knows that very well, from that great majority of his life in which he was not a Kamper, whatever his supposed rank then in the regiment of work. How often back then did *he* sit and fume in his little nippy motor-car and with Better Things To Do, behind the toiling of some underpowered rig up a narrow country road, or even in the wrong lane of a motorway? How often had he been powerless to escape that fat idiot's slowness, the fat girth around which nothing could easily be seen – alongside which, any car driver's reluctant to risk meeting his Maker by overtaking, however tempted? Fat idiot. Fat idiot. Can't you see this line of traffic behind you? Pull over, can't you, you selfish, insensitive pillock, and let the world get past you, and on with its real working life!

And now – look! – that beautiful hillside, that gorgeous bay – who on *earth* ever allowed them to put a *caravan*-site *there*?!

Oh yes, he muses, shaking his head. He's certainly thought and said all that. In his time. Over and over. But now – when that lorry hisses behind him on the hill in the endless roadworks, all lights blazing, or when that impatient Neapolitan in his nice black sporty Golf is swerving like Schumacher all over Lotte's back end – he smiles and says: I'm doing the best I can... Don't give yourself a heart-attack...

When he sees those lines of caravans on the cliff, he will consider driving past in search of a site less obtrusive, so that he won't feel quite so bad (but then again, the next place might not have wi-fi).

And when he's shuffling in and out of a space on the edge of an English supermarket car-park, the eyes of several trolley-toting regular shoppers distended to gobstoppers by sheer outrage, he'll steadily continue his re-reverse. He wouldn't be *trying* to fit in this space if he didn't know he can *eventually* do it. She's manoeuvrable in the extreme is Lotte, and not really as big as she looks either. And you know you're not just staring at me in disbelief at my gall in entering your stable little world. You *really* want to live this life *yourself*, don't you? Admit there's more than a little envy in your despising stare.

So, when Lotte's gearing is just a little too ponderous for you on that climb; or when she joins that too-conspicuous herd near your favourite place of natural beauty, already preparing mentally, as he parks her, to move on again; or when she's as wide as a double-parking delivery van in the market-town main street, but can clearly be held to have less needful business there – at these times, he has to admit, he does start to feel the buzz of achieving Bad Boy status. It's come to him quite late in life. Why should he not enjoy it while he can?

He tries to cheer himself by creating vengefully in his head a two-dimensional stereotype – the Alfa-Male (geddit?): *"Do you not understand, English, I have an expenses claim to create this very afternoon in a Florentine cafe, some perfunctory business to complete and a mistress to see to before the sun sets?..."*

OK, OK, he says, and Lotte agrees, gutturally, automatically changing down again with a discreet cough and Les-Dawson-hitch of her bosom. We will maintain our dignity, they agree, and be patient. It isn't easy. The road gets steeper and hotter and busier and well, obviously, *higher*. Lotte's radiator-fan keeps fluttering into action and he imagines her a little redder in the face. And on setting off he'd stupidly, ignorantly, imagined a nice soft road through vineyards!

Then suddenly – oh, fantastic – as if you thought it couldn't get worse – roadworks! Single-lane. Lotte straining not to allow any onlooker to suspect that her underwear is steaming. Stop. Start. Stop. Start. Grind.

Sniffing now hot, new tarmac, as well as diesel-fumes and dust. Stop. Start.

Stop. Start.

Stop. Start. Tunnel.

Finally through a haze of fumes, a more expansive vista starts to appear before them. Hairpins and tunnels are now beginning to twist downward, through the grey exhaust-fume. Easier for Lotte, but still no fun.

So now, after a pause (*servizio autostradale*) for a coffee and a sandwich – at last, they're into the *Tangentiale Firenze*, where efficient, speedy traffic cranks up again out of other wider, tidal tunnels. Now he's peering, cursing, for signs, sliding hopefully from lane to lane... Ultimately, mid afternoon, pressure starts to ease off, and he's picked his gyratory way just a few kilometres south of the great city. He can soon stop being a raving road-and-van-bore.

A few extra manoeuvres – he's copied directions from Mike's earlier email onto a post-it-note stuck on the steering-wheel, and he's rolling down the broad entrance-drive into a big, bright campsite, and – hey! There they are, the "girls" at any rate – the long-hyped-rendezvous with good ole friends...

Chapter 17

*Old friends – Lindberg 1927 – how embarrassing – and a day in gentle rain –
and a day in Florence doing the Art*

Next morning. Coffee, of course. And Mike has just walked past, up top on
the path – the Captain caught him in the corner of his eye as he put down
the kettle.

Mike's the one who used to suggest driving to Blackpool, as they turned
off the M62 to teach those kids in the middle of Manchester instead, back
in the 1970s – good ole pal Mike, recently himself a motor-homer. He's off
on his way to the showers, in a hooded brown top, a towel over his arm.
It's raining, but he's not using a brolly, any more than the Captain was ten
minutes ago. This is Italian springtime rain, not English rain of any time of
the year.

It's been raining gently, pretty much all night – sprinkling on Lotte's lid
since he went to bed well after midnight. It's really his first rain since he
arrived on the continental mainland. Only a couple of weeks or so ago, he
was having his last-minute worries before casting the die and heading for
Portsmouth – and now he's pleased that this feels as if there'll be another
break from serious driving for a few days.

If he'd driven Lotte by the most direct route from Bilbao to Florence, he
would have covered 884 miles, and that's about 1,400 km in new money. In
fact, already swerving a bit in Provence, and again around the Italian Lakes,
to say nothing of the odd little excursion while "resting", he's actually done a
helluva lot more than that distance.

Anyway, yesterday he'd phoned ahead to confirm the meeting-up, and then
timed his arrival perfectly. Mike's wife Maggie, and mutual friends Graham

and Susan (from so long ago it feels like another life, as does the whole of that first teaching job in Manchester), had hung around Site Reception and delightedly greeted him, up through the side window that he slid open from his cockpit seat. Mike, of course, was hanging back, for effect – "cooking".

It was wonderful to see those happy old faces. Then he'd hopped out happily himself, to register at Reception, and back to the van to drive round and find a space – which reminds him now that he needs to go back to the office and tell the staff the number of the pitch he's chosen. Lotti's on the terraced level discreetly just below Mike and Maggie's larger, brand-new, double-axled rig.

He's still congratulating himself on his poise, timing and stamina: turning up just as planned yesterday, and after that horrible road! At the same time he has to have in his head that, even allowing for a three-day stop here to explore Florence again (an old favourite place of his) he has his next main rendezvous to achieve in two more weeks time: at the far end of Sicily, Trapani, to pick up his darling youngest, Freya, from her Ryanair flight.

And: that then he needs to be back up in Sorrento, another ten days after that! To give away Laura to Ian, in their romantic wedding-location. Yes, and Freya to be a bridesmaid, along with her eldest sister Emma. All these folks flying out, the bride and groom, the other family-members on both sides, plus the Muse's old friend Jerry the photographer, close to the Wedding Day. Volcanic ash-clouds permitting…

And he's reminded himself he also planned to visit, in this next three weeks, on the way down, or perhaps with Freya coming back up, some of those places in the southern half of mainland Italy and Sicily that his Dad flew from (and/or bombed) sixty-seven years previously. He won't admit it, yet – but somewhere that's *still* feeling too much – even more ambitious now than it felt planning it, and when embarking from Portsmouth, and landing in Bilbao, or arriving in Ariege …

He won't think about it. Concentrate just on completing the journey, maybe. Anything more – the history, the father – consider a bonus. Reason argues that, time and motion, the drive itself will easily be do-able. Oh, the post-ablutions coffee is good today. He's also prompted by his inner economic demon that at some point he must calculate the cost in diesel-gallons of his trip so far. It is a question to be asked and answered, and he's the only one to do it.

Anyway. Mike and Maggie. They've been together a good long time now. They split up with their first spouses, and got together with each other, at about the same time that Emma and Laura's mother, the Captain's first partner, lit out for the Hebrides, leaving him holding the babies, or at least the primary school-kids. M and M have been together ever since though, so – Respect for that: unlike the Captain, who, fifteen years after his first divorce, had gone plummeting into his *second*... Once more into the volcano, dear friends... Life, eh? But he doesn't want to do any more reflecting on that just now – this young wedding coming up will doubtless force it upon him soon enough.

He wonders though, whether all relationships that achieve the longevity of Mike and Maggie's settle into a pattern that is unkind to one partner or the other. If so, in this case maybe it's Maggie – though of course in every relationship there's always some kind of collusion. Maggie having almost been killed by a freak event five years ago Mike, taking overall responsibility, sometimes overdoes it …

Now Mike and Graham have appeared at his window. They're going to the site supermarket. Would he like to join them? He goes along, buying milk, bread, butter and bottled water while they grab much more. He's buying for one man, camping. They're buying for four people in a mobile mansion. And would he like to have breakfast with them this morning?

Oh – no thanks – bit zonked – long drive yesterday …

Oh well OK then mate, you just chill …

And indeed he will. They tell him he's invited later to an evening meal under their large awning – Graham and Maggie will cook.

He, of course assents, but why is he so slow? No mystery there, he thinks – too long in his own company, not having to string words together and be sociable. Has he actually got a bit depressed as well as tired, the system a bit slowed down? He was looking forward to meeting his friends; but could it be that he was mainly looking forward to The Meeting itself, to his landing, this time like Lindberg in 1927, punctually at this once-dreamed and distant field, leaning and waving from the cockpit, engine still running, leaning down to kiss the old "girls"? Forgetting to anticipate, in the background, a little male rivalrousness?

Just think, too, Captain: in your English homes, Mike and Maggie, you and the Muse, only live fifty miles apart, and – actually – how *often* do you choose to meet them back *there*? Once or twice a year, maximum. There has to be a reason for that…

… And in fact, not at all, last year, he reckons, thinking about it some more.

Is it, thinking about it now, that Mike is actually a bit competitive, in a way the Captain likes to believe *he* isn't? Such as: the Captain retires, buys Lotte; Mike sees Lotti, retires, buys an up-to-the-minute, bigger, double-rear-axled rig, complete with awning and all mod cons. Including, for instance, a built-in oven, much more versatile than Lotte's modest worktop-hob. Yes, really a home-standard oven, look mate – in and upon which a full dinner can be created for four, and served under an awning where there's room to stretch out legs and feet while sipping the *vino rosso*.

They always knew one another so well, he and Mike, in the old days, discussing relationships, children, football and work – always work. Can it be that they really had less in common, without the work, and beyond that particular place and time of life, than he's ever previously thought? They're all "retired now", these four – though all still busy in their own ways. Graham and Susan, though, have always mainly been Mike's mates, since all the way back in their schooldays, in fact.

So – ach – is it really for *their* benefit (but he could surely have approached it differently) that Mike now, suddenly, over the food, over the wine, comes up with:

"One thing I've never quite got though, matey" – he's talking to the Captain – "he went to Oxford University you know, this feller" (theatrical aside to the other two) – "is why, matey, you went into teaching in a Manchester comp after that. How come you got into that, because aren't I right in thinking you got a First?" This line of questioning is all a show, a put-on, surely? Because he surely knows the answer? It feels more than a bit… patronising? Or… worse?

"Actually "a good Second" is what they called it, Mike. Someone told me afterwards I nearly got a First. Anyway that's all a long time ago."

"So anyway – but how did you end up *just teaching* after that?"

This man was, for quite a lot of years, first a teaching colleague, then what the Captain would back then have called one of his closest friends. He could say to himself, well, maybe this is just Mike trying to make me talk. Or maybe, mystified, the other two've been asking Mike about it? But no, in fact it just seems to the Captain as if Mike himself, after all these years, all those conversations, *doesn't get it himself.*

Just teaching.

The Captain feels now, for the first time, how incomprehensible his life has always been even to those who, he would have said, "know me well". He has to run *that* by his *friend – again*?

Even as he answers levelly, his stomach sinks – and a cold, dull anger starts to rise. He supposes, Mike, that it was probably politics. Ideals, Mike. People had them then. He felt he had that luxury then, he supposes a lot of people did. He thought it might make a difference, he might make a difference. In the sense, in those days, of the public service. There was such a thing, in those days, still, wasn't there?

The three are looking at him and he is conscious suddenly that *they* now live in the new Present, in a time when they can't possibly, if ever they did, think that way any longer, even about another time in their own lives – forty years ago, nearly, now. Times have changed.

How embarrassing.

Can it be that he can still live in that past? Or is it that they actually *never* thought that way, and certainly can't be expected to get it now, on their holiday, in this great big camper, on a warm, wine-cradling evening near Florence? If so, don't ask the question. Let's make believe that time is just one long, warm, wine-cradling moment.

How *was he supposed* to answer? Perhaps he should, in honour of the present state of the world, say, If only he had known... ha, ha!... probably with a string of self-deprecating jokes... but that ain't going to happen, Matey. He thinks: it would actually make more sense if he started burbling about stocks and shares, about which none of them (probably?) know anything. That would at least be a safer shared subject for speculation right now.

These people were *there*. They were actually a living part of the past he lived in, too – but that fact apparently needs to be reconfigured, now, for this audience, as "Living In The Past" – say, on the one hand, nostalgically, sentimentally – and/or, on the other, as if we now realise *that* was always a retarded, damaged place ...

And also these people seem to believe that since they are now richer, and life is easier for them, the world has become a better place; and the past, irrelevant. This is such a common and pervasive assumption among his generation, that he has to work hard not to feel very crazy, very singular, very alone – as finally he lays himself out, later this night, on Lotte's rear bench seat to sleep.

The next morning, the others are off for the day to San Giminiano. It's a nice place, they've heard, interesting, picturesque. Maggie gives him a shout. "We're off now. Are you *sure* you don't want to come? Well anyway – if you get fed up, don't forget you can always come across here, and sit under the awning."

"Thanks. I won't get fed up".

They're talking to him now, as if he's the old man! The point is they don't get him, and that's OK, because he knows by now he's not easily "got". He thinks, *I've tried all my life not to become a cliché. Maybe that's been my one, true, precious (in every sense of the word, maybe) ambition. And I think I proved, last night, that I've achieved it. If only to myself.*

Yep. So. Almost the only home-grown company that he reliably *doesn't* get fed up with, apart from The Muse or his daughters these days, is his own. He can have arguments, and get upset with, himself or his situation – feeling old, getting himself lost, hurting himself, a poor choice of campsite, bad mountain traffic on bad roads, miserable weather if he gets any. But he won't allow himself to be tired of his *own* company. That would be the end, and he can't end here. Too much to do. He'll jolly and cajole himself, or call himself a fool, and just get on with it with a bit of a grin. He's got beyond the point where anything (that isn't another uncomprehending person) will get on his nerves.

And lord, can people get on his nerves! In fact these trips, this trip, are as much to get away from the irritating presence of his own countryfolk, as for any other reason. He reminds himself, doggedly: this trip will be in order to visit a land and a skyline that his dad flew over many years ago, at war; and to have some time travelling with his youngest daughter; and to see another married, and the third, the eldest, big with child, in attendance too. He'll learn more and more about Italy, about Europe. He'll do some more research on that war-time history, and on planning the challenging near-future, pretty soon today. All that's his authentic task. Not this.

But first, he must acknowledge: here he is. And it was *planned*! He's started, so he'll finish, this stopover. He'll be here a few days, he'll exchange evenings and drinks again with his friends. They'll visit the Uffizi together tomorrow, they've agreed now, and maybe do something else together the next day. He won't kid himself that he isn't in one way glad: for a day or so to have stopped driving; to be in one place again for a bit.

And so when, for today, those others've taken themselves off, then he's relieved to have a chance to stop, to read, to write, in a word to reflect, in a place wiped clean again of foreign, English tongues. He's by himself at last, and has nothing to do but that. Just Be, by himself again. Listen to Italian sparrows, woodpigeons – and springtime rain speckling his roof.

Why would solitude not be a joy to this man? Maybe all those years ago he made a choice, a strong, very social choice of career – and once embarked upon it, had said, I've started, so I'll finish. And maybe more and more he had come to think, And at the end of it, there'll be a pension, payments which now reliably and regularly arrive while he decides what to do and who to be next. Because he knows very well *that* job wasn't the *only* thing he could have done; and *that* man then wasn't the *only* man he could be. Now, he's had his kids; has a few real good friends and is lucky in the most marvellous partner. The fact is, he's been up to his neck for thirty or more of his fifty-eight years in other people, including his partners, kids and their needs – and he's been very open, very vulnerable to them. The wonderful daughters are now all grown and almost flown. Now, belatedly, he can do his own growing and flying. How many new potentials, ideas, lives and skills, new arts and experiences can he feed into this one lifetime that he's been given? One lifetime doesn't have to imply only one life. He has more versatility than that. There was always more to him, there was always going to be.

He knows that being a hairy old man in a camper might fit into many people's ideas of a sad cliché, but he feels he knows how far wide of the mark that is. Meeting his friends here, however irritating (they are, after all, people who do know him better than most and still in many ways don't understand him, so how should they be anything but delightfully, familiarly, irritating?) – meeting them again underlines at least to him that if nothing else, he knows he's actually evaded capture by what they'll always only see as that stereotype.

And so he knows that as they all joke and break bread together again over the next couple of days, it may well sometimes be in mutual incomprehension. He has been, and isn't any more now really, one of them. Whatever, he knows there was always a great deal more than one person for him to be.

The next day, they go and "do" Florence. By which is meant, first he makes it clear he's buying dinner at the end of the day to repay somewhat for the two they've now insisted on cooking for him in their lovely oven, and served under their palatial awning. So they visit the Duomo and photograph themselves in front of its more-than-licorice-allsort facades. Then they split up, so that while they go inside that echoing cavern, he can visit the Michaelangelo David in the Academia, though he's much more interested in the "Slaves". Then he hustles on, to another unfinished Buonarotti, the "Pieta Bandini" in the Museo dell'Opera del Duomo – and then unexpectedly gets entranced by the extraordinary collection of biblical Donatellos in there.

Then they meet up again outside the Uffizi – beneath the other – the copy – David in the square.

After predictably-awful haggling and hassling, discovering that their expensive pre-bought Tickets only buy them a place at the end of a three-hour queue, they eventually get in (this is indeed "industrial tourism" on an obscene scale) by parting with still more dosh. The truth of the Uffizi is just as he was forewarned, and the best view it offers – through football-match-size crowds in rooms in any case far too dingy for viewing those Botticellis – is the elevated one outwards from the high windows, out and down the Arno to the Ponte Vecchio.

Take a breath, then down in the Piazza again, Mike gets his photo taken, gurning next to a performance-artist painted white and posing as a sculptured chubby Cupid.

Finally, the four eat a forgettable but nonetheless overpriced plate of tourist meatballs and pasta together at his expense. They're all cheerful because, despite the strenuousness of the day, Florence has been Done, as agreed, and they all have the cheerful photographs to prove it.

Chapter 18

Ossaia – different friends – bones – angels – a stone & some ghosts

The next day, to Lotte's relief (she was getting bored as she always does on big commercial sites) he makes his farewells and hits the road His foot's down, and she gobbles the A1, the major route towards Rome, drawing it through pursed lips like a last strand of spaghetti. But not *for* Rome. No – and probably not at all. A detour a little way south, in the direction of Perugia, will take the Captain towards Lago Trasimeno, and one particular small village on its north-western tip, Ossaia. Bill and Tina have asked him to stop in on his way. They're not Mike and Meg.

If the Captain is to start acclimatising to thoughts of war and its trauma, then this is one of the many places Italy will offer him for contemplation of the extensive history of human slaughter. Lago Trasimeno is that very same Trasimene Lake beside which, during the second Punic War, Hannibal's transalpine expeditionary force created its simple but brutal ambush for a defensive Roman army led by its impulsive consul, Flaminius. The story is that the Romans were drawn forward along the northern shore of the lake by the sight of fires lit at Hannibal's order on distant hilltops – to give the impression that his army was much further off. Then the Carthaginian force, in fact hidden in the forest above the Roman army's road, fell upon them. No elephants, frostbitten or otherwise, were required to effect a straightforward massacre. Of Flaminius' army of 40,000 it is known that 15,000 were killed that day; of the Carthaginians, possibly only 2,500 of 50,000.

Many of Lago Trasimeno's local place-names seem still to speak about the aftermath for the defenders – Sepultaglia, and the stream called Sanguineto, speak for themselves. As does Ossaia –"place of bones", "charnel".

But today, the little village of Ossaia is ticking brilliantly in the midday heat, and Lotte idles beside the local trattoria while the Captain double-checks a new set of transcribed directions. Is the early summer dust here even whiter, for ancient extra calcium content?

Yes, his friends' house is just up there – up this hill, on which there is a tasteful little cemetery, a modern one, newly-walled in stone. And here are Bill and Tina to greet him – as he carefully circles his wagon in front of their villa. These are in fact old friends of The Muse. He's been here with her before. They are quiet, considerate. They're pleased to see him, to discuss the road, the route, the history. Then they wander down together to the trattoria for pizza; and on the walk back he dawdles a little behind them and peers through the gateway into that local Garden of Rest, all neat walls and fresh flowers. Here the gathered dusk is studded with flickering oil-lamps, and niched candles newly-lit in glowing red jars.

The Captain reflects that his dad, when his time came twenty-five years ago, and his mum, much more recently, both opted with typical lack of egotism to be cremated, and to be "scattered" in their local Garden of Remembrance – anonymous, unfocused, institutional lawns, shrubbery, roses, lawns – beside the modern crematorium on the hillside above their home town. In an earlier time it might have been said they had gone, like poor Mozart, "to an unmarked grave". Most certainly they, the parents, would have said that a nightly (or a weekly, or even an annual) chore of lighting a candle for them would be "much too much fuss and bother". They were low-church, she originally C of E, he a Methodist. To him, *all* ritual was understood to be "Empty Ritual". On this topic, as on much that might be labelled "the Spiritual", their second son the Captain remains at least ambivalent. He does though probably share their view that caring for the living is much more onerous and therefore praiseworthy than performing a later symbolic act, more for oneself than for the deceased …

Anyway, next, it's wonderful – with Lotte close outside the window – to sleep in a big, soft bed, in a big, elegant, solid Italian house, in a large double-room shared with various framed-reproduction Fra Angelicos, including that beautiful Annunciation, the angel with the rainbow-feathered wings.

Early the next morning he climbs further up their hill, followed by the sun, holding the anticipation of a peaceful breakfast by the pool and more of last evening's considered conversation. Near the top, the sun's growing heat sits him down for a moment on a wayside rock. Thus it's entirely by chance, while meditating momentarily upon the events of 217 BC, that his stopping-place gives him a sudden face-to-face reading-view of a rough slab of rock, engraved to commemorate the deaths of twenty-seven Italian partisans – right here, at the hands of the Germans on their retreat north, in 1944.

He heads off from their goodbyes, confident he'll be back there soon with the Muse.

But as he drives ever southward, it's towards an army of grim spirits. The Allies of Autumn 1943, having crossed the Med with their Air Forces in support, advance with dogged difficulty northward.

Chapter 19

A plateau "high" – Sulmona –Milligan, Sassoon – Roccaraso – 'Museo' – liminal awakening – Schloss Lotte – Castel di Sangro – a plaque

Anyway, after fond farewells to good friends, this day he's trundling patiently across on the A25, from Terni towards Sulmona. It's a beautiful, quiet, highland road, graced by an occasional whispering Audi or solitary lorry on the opposite carriageway.

There's nothing quite so escapist as driving a gently-undulating, well-surfaced road across a plateau. He's moved to jump down a couple of times to take useless, uncapturable photographs such as incompetent amateurs like him always take in these places, only to look at them again on return to the homeland and wonder why they ever bothered to stop and snap such featureless pieces of landscape. What he's been trying to take is a photograph of – simple, travelling contentment; and as this is something deep in his heart, it's something his little digital Olympus is unlikely to be able to record.

The pleasure, he must admit to himself, is partly an afterglow from Ossaia and partly because (and not in spite) of the fact that this is a leg of the journey on which he needs simply to be covering ground. He's already done so today, substantially, and there's more to do before nightfall. He feels at last that the Steinbeckian Quest is on, or that in Sherlock Holmes parlance, "the game's afoot". Not quite here, not yet, but around just a few hundred more corners. So he can justify the insincerity of his regret at not really stopping to look, at glancing merely through a screen on a major road, and twice only through a camera; at conversing monosyllabically, at a service-station, and not – either with satisfaction or irritation – among friends. All his conversation here's with himself, in grunts, grins and half-phrases, and with Lotte's continuous mumbling upon tarmac. Last night the guidebook told him that somewhere near that last little motorway tunnel lies the town of Cocullo, where they still celebrate a weird ancient festival involving snakes... but that's gone now, behind him. Pity he hadn't got time!

And so across, around Sulmona (birthplace of the Roman poet Ovid) to connect with the S17 – and then south: into mountainous Abruzzo. He's beginning, in more ways than one, to be on a high. The Book says there's a campsite open all the year round at Roccaraso; so now, near the end of his day, he flogs on along the occasionally-cavernous gorge of the River Gizio in falling darkness, on a road which by now requires more squinting attention than is comfortable...

In the guidebooks, Roccaraso is mostly an alpine-sports venue; especially documented as such in newreels from the 1930s, when the most glamorous aristocrats and *Fascisti* shooshed down its pistes. However, when the Germans established a headquarters here a few short years later, in 1943, came the town's darkest 20th century moment. Heavy bombing (by the USAAF) destroyed 90% of the place. Then, for revenge, the Germans destroyed the nearby village of Pietransieri – killing 127 civilians.

Ah. And now, forward among the advancing British ghosts: Cyril – flying his last few sorties over this area in December 1943. And in January '44, the arrival of a certain L/Bdr. Terence "Spike" Milligan and his artillery-crew, not far south of here, heading toward the Sangro River through horrible mud and torrential rain, on the Allied winter "push" north from the Salerno landings. He and his pals, not yet even dug into their new positions, can hear the rumble of gunnery as the "PBI" (universal slang: Poor Bloody Infantry) get pounded by enemy artillery ahead. They consider the carnage of what they know is the uphill, exposed slog of their Tommy comrades. Spike suddenly has in his head those lines from the still relatively recent, Great War – in which his father had served: Sassoon's poem of the motorised drive-through by a British General.

'He's a cheery old fellow,' said Harry to Jack,

As they slogged up to Arras to rifle and pack.

But he did for them both with his plan of attack.

Spike has also, he says, been reading Wilfred Owen. (In his 1960s youth, the Captain had seen the Great War as very distant; the Second, pretty recent. One of the things that time and age does, is to make him realise that the twenty years between 1919 and 1939 would not have felt like a very long time at all, to those who lived it in their youth.) "Mussolini – His Part In My Downfall" is Spike's final book of WWII recollections – a series maybe best-known for its dashes of Goon-humour. The Captain, though, reckons this particular volume is also one of the most absorbing warts-and-all depictions of the *longueurs* and horrors of army life at war[1]. Before the book's culminating event, Milligan, suffering severe premonitions of his own mortality, would find himself waking one morning to write in his diary: "I died for the England I dreamed of, not the England I know".

Oh – rats! – but back in the present, in today's very dusk, the guidebook-alluring 'always-open' campsite at Roccaraso is firmly *fermata* – tchah! – and looks as if it will be for months. The town, like many ski-resorts out of season, is drab, grey, accursed. So he *can't* stop here. He doesn't pause for longer than the cursing of padlocked gates requires, and flogs onward, his eyes suddenly very tired. Another, and another, little tunnel, each more ill-lit than the last, seem actively to want to hypnotise him with repetitive, grimy lights, their road-slabs' rhythmic clunks under his wheels.

His plateau-driving 'high' now thoroughly dispelled, the Captain knows he must stop very soon, or be seduced, struggling vainly, into nodding – and then a tunnel-wall, a tree or a wheel-churning leap into that vicious little gorge. 'Castel di Sangro', a sign says – and, to the right, a turning: for '*Museo*'. '*Museo*' can equal nothing more than 'empty car-park' at this time of evening. So he brakes and turns quickly off the road and along a smooth, narrow little track, pulling on the handbrake and stopping Lotte's engine.

And dowses the headlights into sudden, complete darkness. His head's still whirring, flashing and clattering on cats' eyes. But now there's just a soothing sound of running water… It's dark enough, about 9.30, and he's certainly not into the town proper, here. Surely can't offend anyone, parked up here, and can move on early in the morning if need be. He draws curtains and blinds, pours himself a quick nip of scotch, pulls out the sleeping-bag and blanket, and crashes out, on Lotte's rear bench-seat, into instant oblivion …

* * *

---

[1]   But see also the brilliant G. MacDonald Fraser: "Quartered Safe Out Here" Harvill Press 1992

When you've pulled in somewhere after dark, just glad enough to stop and sleep and remove the perils of the road, there's always a few moments of concern, as you slip back into morning consciousness. What will the pitch-dark stopping-place have *become*, in this new daylight? That's the question-mark in the sleeping-bag.

And here, now … There's a crunching on gravel of steady strides approaching his van, there's a cough and a softly-spoken word of command.

Oh dear …

Then the footsteps continue past him, a couple of feet from his head, without so much as a pause to indicate that Lotte's presence has even caused an eyebrow to be raised. Now, when he gingerly parts a front curtain, he sees: wow, some "car-park"! An expanse of misty green meadow beside a stream, a white stone building – evidently the Museo – a tethered horse grazing in the middle distance; and a man on the track by the stream calling repetitively now, throwing a stick for his big silly black dog, first on the bank, now even splashing into the water … Their regular walk before breakfast. In the background a mile away, a tree-clad hill rises, and graduates into blurry brown scrub. Nearer, a modern sculpture of a man poised in the act of casting a fly. The *Museo* is apparently for the history of fishing on the Sangro... Above and beyond that, a dark mountain-peak swims in and out of grey cloud.

So. Here he is.

Now. He is – here. Awakening in new, liminal space.

Impulsive night-time stopping of the van can sometimes afford just this opportunity to find oneself, a few hours' sleep later, peering out into an unplanned new-dawn landscape. While Lotte the camper-van is his aircraft or lunar module, viewed externally she avoids any obvious out-of-place-ness. She may be a means of space-travel; but she's also – to the passer-by – just a vehicle, parked, that wasn't parked here yesterday. And to her camping occupant, the great advantage is that she isn't a tent, otherwise Bowser out there would by now have been snuffling alarmingly in his earthbound, tremulous ear-holes.

No, the Captain's in a field; at home; here, off the ground; and enclosed, in unassuming *Schloss Lotte*, the Moving Castle.

After the dog-walker's done and gone, the Captain steps out and around his van to seek out the full panorama, and to check from all her sides into which

Castell di Sangro: Museo, car-park, angling statue and distant Lotte
[photo: the author]

quarter of the compass he, in his turn, can piss without offence. Across the stream is the town, a half-mile walk away. Back on the main road he can see its first houses drawing his eye towards quiet blocks of taller buildings in rising chimney-smoke and beyond them to another imposing hill, backed by more, and more, grey, grim mountains.

Castel di Sangro: translation of an inscription at the Town Hall:

> *'On 7 November 1943 the Germans blew up the whole town to slow the advance of Allied forces that fought here for the next 8 months to break through the German defenses on the coast of Monte Arazzecca and on top of Colle di San Giovanni and Castello Superiore, as part of the famous "Gustav Line".*

> *'This radical destruction resulted in yet another Diaspora of the inhabitants, who had survived the enemy and helped the Allied advance with a daring inadequately recognized by the late bronze medal for valor awarded at the Town Hall.*

'The citation for this medal reads:

"Fearlessly resisted the bombing and the harassment of the invading enemy, suffering heavy losses of human lives and material goods. October 1943 – May 1944."

You can't but taste the bitter acid with which that plaque was inscribed. "Daring inadequately recognised"; "The bombing and harassment of the invading enemy".

And "enemy"? Who is referred to here, as "enemy"?

Why, everybody.

Everybody not Italian. The status of Italy, after her armistice/surrender in 1943 was at best ambiguous, at worst non-existent.

Their great claim at this time to our sympathy is that they remained, as a generality and to a remarkable extent, staunchly humane. In all their fear and privations Italians still (as documented by many more than Eric Newby) continued to perform quiet heroics in hiding servicemen on both sides who were in the wrong place, desperate to evade capture behind enemy lines. Many, many Italians helped human beings who were not Italian but who simply caught at their pity. German reprisals for resistance operations – in Rome and in mountain villages all over northern Italy – killed hundreds, at the very least, of innocent people including women and children. Meanwhile they struggled to achieve all the practical compromises which might keep themselves alive, while Allied bombing killed thousands.

"Daring inadequately recognised"? He's starting to agree.

Chapter 20

Barrea – Pasetta – a bad feeling – a boy's escape and return – back to the
Log – meeting 223 again – Isernia? – earthquakes, crossroads and history –
air-raids and civilians – speechless

After half a day in Castel di Sangro, the drive up the valley, the climb round
a couple of high scarps, wasn't far. *This* campsite *was* open. The view from
the hillside, over the roofs to the long high lake, Barrea and the surrounding
mountains – enfoldingly-beautiful, calm, restful. So he can't say it's been a
hard day. Lotti's climbed another thousand feet of winding highway, and
now he's not far below the elevation of far-off Ben Nevis. But getting out
and walking to vantage with his camera, he surely can't blame this sudden
slump in energy and morale on such minor altitude? All he can say is, he's
feeling weak.

These mountains, this lake, these towering sunset clouds. The Sublime.
He's stuck gawping and snapping again – just an old-fashioned, outmoded
tourist-Romantic, looking forward through a view-finder: ultimately to
a wedding by Vesuvius. A daughter to be married. Another with child.
Another just-left childhood, a student on her first solo flight – through a
volcanic ash-cloud?

Yes, it's back. The Future – with so much, close-to, for him to look forward
to – in the bigger picture still feels dangerous, and to carry a more difficult
set of potentials than he ever wanted for his children, or grandchildren-to-
be …

Well, and here really *is* the Present – here is Pasetta.

This is the man who owns and runs the campsite. Almost as if in mockery
of so tremulous a visitor, he bounces out, in his mountain-man's jutty beard

and cap. When the Captain totters down to the Office, the sheer flint-eyed jollity of this man, his solidity of handshake, belie his years. He must be at least ten years older than Kamper, by his story – well, indeed, by his book[1], which he sells and inscribes with aplomb to this latest of his international guests. Mountain-guide and self-styled promoter of Abruzzo, Pasetta is the uncrowned popular king of these parts, hero of climbs in the Himalaya, of stories of wolves and bears, of skiing championships and even of uphill Giro d'Italia stages. He's enjoyed himself, over the years, by becoming widely known for stunts like popping up unbidden on TV beside a winter-sports or cycling presenter, or at the elbow of the gasping, triumphant finisher – dressed improbably, Davy-Crockett-like, in Abruzzan wolfskins. His book's photographs prove all this true, and he'll sign and sell the photographically-illustrated volume to every visitor who'll have it.

Thus Pasetta has appointed himself both trademark and salesman of a poor, patronised, unvisited region in urgent need of economic generators. You may at first wish to see him, as box-gogglers of Italy's northern cities no doubt do, as a bit of a clown. But – expert mountain-guide, celebrated long-distance walker and declamatory poetaster – like all shrewd mountain-men, he knows exactly what the game is. With limited education and opportunity, out of an early childhood interrupted by the war and a young adulthood stunted by a tough period of emigration to the USA, this man returned to his homeland roots to remake himself. Unselfconsciously, he acts out a visibility on behalf of his people and their dignity. He can stand ignorant condescension. His shoulders shrug it like mountain weather.

Today he's been found on what might be called a quiet day at home. The campsite front-office wall is being renewed. His son's around too, keeping things ticking. All day while you're near the site, Pasetta's growling chatter is audible, on the phone to prospective campers, or to the builders. He's so bloody fit. Ten years older than you, Captain. Hard as nails, as bright and sharp as the local sparrows.

Captain? He just maunders about, taking his photographs, feeling weedy, irritated, disorganised, nervous, undecided and – for the first time this trip? – actually lonely.

Weedy: His legs have gone watery. Is he unwell? Something's wrong.

---

[1]   Tommaso D'Amico 2009 *Pasetta raconta* – Grafica Isernina

Irritable: In all his admiration for the man and the place, he's actually at the same time feeling alienated, by a land that is so determinedly itself, its own place that makes no compromises to the outsider, especially to the soft city-dweller.

Disorganised: Thanks to the re-routing from Roccaraso, it's starting to feel too improvised and accidental that he's here at all. But once again, where else *should* he be? He can't get off this particular train of events now.

Nervous: this feels too high, too free, too random, too uncontained. He may be a free molecule, but just now, it feels as if all his particles are evaporating into the ether.

And so, finally, Lonely: which encompasses all the rest: weedy, irritable, disorganised, nervous loneliness – a feeling that he is missing everything and everyone, especially his partner, that could ever contain him. And Missing the Point. Something's wrong. Something's going to go wrong.

Unable to stay with this present moment, then, he starts to read Pasetta's book:

'I, Tomaso d'Amico, known as "Pasetta", was born in Barrea … . on February 2nd, 1941, at 4.30pm. Barrea counted 1,500 inhabitants at that time. I'm the seventh son of eight …

'I was two-and-a-half years old, when, during World War II, the German troops, in retreat from the Allied forces, occupied Barrea, forcing me and my family to leave home. That was October 28th 1943. We left for Bisegna, 40km from Barrea; that was to be my second home.

'By the end of the occupation we were glad to go back home. But mines placed along the road made a tragedy of our march. Lots of people lost their lives.

'When finally we came back to our devastated and plundered homes, our major problem was to find a place to sleep. We had no beds, so I and my smallest brother had to sleep in a large dressing-table. The first and third drawers were taken out so that we could breathe. He slept above me. Often he peed … '

Ah. So that's the point of all this! It is going right!

The Captain's head is immediately recalibrated, sent straight to his other book.

Log Book: July-August 1943:

Ops 57 – bombing Cassino[2] – as the crow flies, west here from Barrea, no more distant than the d'Amicos' refuge of Bisegna, in the opposite direction

Ops 59 – bombing Vairano – 20 miles down the A1 from Cassino

Ops 60 – bombing Venafro – between Cassino and Vairano

Ops 61 –bombing Isernia – the nearest large town to Barrea, just 20 miles south-east

Ops 64, 65, 66 – bombing Cantalupo nel Sannio; Carpinone; Acquafondata: tiny villages, the first two on the railway, the third a strategic high point east of Cassino.

---

[2]   In what was the bloodiest corner of the whole campaign, *this* "Cassino" was the town of that name, and not Monte Cassino, the monastery and nearby German stronghold a thousand feet above it.

All these places form an arc within thirty miles of where he's parked right now.

In fact, Pasetta's family were forced out of their home in Barrea just two months before the Captain's Dad was sent back to England, and Milligan's mob sent north. The Allied air- and land-offensive, on Isernia and this whole strategic triangle near the Volturno, was what had forced the Germans back up into the next lot of mountains, and thus the d'Amicos out of their home.

Now the Captain tries to grab his focus back. OK. He should base himself here in Barrea for a few days: regroup, plan, research. Immediately, he jolts Lotte out of her afternoon nap and heads off down into the valley. OK. Isernia? Isernia.

Isernia is actually, he learns, a *very* ancient town – and site. Remarkable remains, perhaps a million years old, of the habitations of proto-human beings, European *homo erectus*, were found lying just below the earth-surface near here. These bits were discovered when the carriageway of the S650 across towards Vasto on the east coast was being laid down.

But Isernians, like the inhabitants of many of the towns in this country, are far less precious about such momentous archeological finds than we English are about unearthing a few flints and potsherds in a hay-field, with a camera-team and a comedy-actor looking on. There have been townships here, in the valley of the Volturno, since the 3rd Century B.C. Isernia was one of the first communities to make a deal with the all-conquering Romans – which gave them equal status as *civites Romani*. There's still a scattering of classical-era masonry in many of the older buildings, and a silent pride in the depth of their history.

But buried sites? Hah. The causes of indigenous indifference to history's disruptions gradually become obvious. This patch, like l'Aquila last year in 2009, like nearby Naples, even like Emilia-Romagna in the north (2012), is earthquake country. Volcanic dust, two significant layers of it, have helped to preserve the bones and tools here. Isernia has in fact been destroyed several times over, even since, relatively-recently, the Romans held sway – quakes in 847, 1349, 1456 and 1805, to name some major ones. A town such as this, rebuilding itself repeatedly from rubble, can't ever be said to forget, or remember, any of its history. The fabric recreates itself, in part from memory, until the next, expected-hopefully-not-too-soon disaster. The fountain in the square today still channels snow-melt water brought down by Roman-era aqueducting from Pasetta's mountains; and its stones are a mixture of ancient, medieval, Renaissance and modern masonry, a higgledy-piggledy assemblage, but a completely authentic map of the 21st Century town's genome.

Much of Isernia has a shabby-modern look nowadays, rather characterless. So many tourist-spots across Europe have their newly-cobbled squares to stroll in, and a network of old-stone streets, an ancient gateway... Many towns in seismic valleys have reasons for bare new-build boxes, and blank open spaces. Isernia is a seismic-valley town.

Sadly, in 1943 it also found itself to be a strategic crossroads.

To put events into context – everyone in UK remembers Coventry, and we all know there was one huge raid when there was a firestorm and the old cathedral went. The population of Coventry then was around 200,000. Actually, there were *three* serious raids on Coventry, between November 1940 and August 1942. Combined death-toll, shocking: overall somewhere in the region of 1,300 ...

Isernia in 1943 featured three important railway-bridges, and it was the keystone to the whole region's hill and valley road and rail systems. On 10th September, it was market day at Isernia. In a raid by USAAF B17s, more than 1,000 Italian civilians[3] were killed in one day, mostly women and children, out of a population probably no greater than 20,000. The main purpose of that raid had been to destroy those railway bridges, so vital to the movement of German armour.

Cyril, perched uncomfortably in his accustomed gun-turret atop of one of the Baltimores of 223 Squadron, RAF Desert Air Force, raided the Volturno region – Cassino, Vairano, Venafro and Isernia – a month later, in mid-October of 1943, towards the end of his tour of duty. These Ops were continual attempts to sever German lines of communication and reinforcement. After the USAAF raids, those bridges still stood, and still needed bringing down. 223 Squadron's crews were probably entirely unaware that Isernia had already been devastated a month earlier. By then, they'd bombed and battered their way across North Africa, hopped across the Med via Malta and Sicily and now found themselves stationed on Italy's heel, at Brindisi. In the circumstances what they were mainly conscious of was the storm of fiercely-concentrated German anti-aircraft fire being put

---

[3]   This is a *sizeable underestimate*, according to contemporary accounts

up in their direction over these towns. And thinking – they must *surely* by now be getting right near the end of their "tour"? – and very jumpy.

Anyway ...

Old Isernia today presents a single, striking piece of twentieth-century public statuary. A classical male nude, distraught, stands up to his ankles in twisted metal and shattered masonry, with a weird whizz-bang of metal-shards flying at his back. That's the memorial. There's little enough reason for Isernia's inhabitants to commemorate historic powerlessness, situated as they are in this earthquake zone. The refusal of these people to sentimentalise any further the events in which such horrors were visited upon their former families is natural enough.

And if they were more assertively to indulge in Remembrance, it wouldn't perhaps be much appreciated by the majority of tourists from – Germany, America, Britain... No, the Captain reckons, here's another town whose reflective endurance deserves memorialising beyond its city-limits.

Meanwhile the "targets", if he's any judge – Look, those *are* the *original* viaducts, surely? – still stand today.

"Bombing results..."

Now he returns once more to the camp-site at Barrea. On sudden impulse now, he calls in to the campsite office, says he needs to move on tomorrow, pays up for his stay and invites the old galoot into Lotti for a glass of wine.

They sit at Lotti's table. He gets out the log-book, and alongside the chapter of Pasetta's childhood, with its family-picture, he opens Cyril's war-record. In Italian much, much worse than Pasetta's out-of-practice Yankee

English, he explains, he's sorry – his dad was involved in the Allied bombing of the towns in this area.

When he gets round to Isernia, Pasetta silently – oh – shakes his head in pain.

There's a pause. The older man takes a couple of sips at the deep-red Montepulciano.

"... But your father – did he get back OK?" he asks.

Chapter 21

Self-interrogation & -justification – about Carlo, Eboli, the south – The Muse – joint-captaincy – bad news – Captain in a spin

So – hang on – he's moving on again – fast! Tomorrow? Suddenly after that?

Well, yes.

But there are those other places?

Yes.

So he'll go that way and look at them, as he has at Isernia?

Well ... but you see ... he can't just serve History. What if he spent a day too long here now, finding out nothing as useful again as that staggering story? And then ... say he had some problem with the van – or there was a delay, or a landslip, on the road south? And then, because of that, say that meant he missed the connection with Freya in Trapani?

Ah. I see. And is he finding – at the very start *of what he came to find – that it's maybe now finding* him *out?*

No. No... Just... Look at the map. At first glance, he's two thirds of the way down Italy. But look at it as road distance! He still has to get across again, down and then curve along the top of the toe of the boot, and that's one long foot. And Sicily after that is big, a very long island, along that northern coast ... And anyway, he'll be coming back up this way from Sicily... well, probably...

And Eboli...

Eboli is important. Yes. Palmi ... They've still got to be done, and they're *definite* stops – as he goes down. And anyway, now, he's told Pasetta he's moving on, so that's fully decided. But he can still maybe look in on Venafro, too, on his way. Cassino: yes OK, but now that's a definite for the way *back*... after the wedding.

OK. Eboli. Quick revision before tomorrow, he reckons.

It was the exiled writer, artist and doctor Carlo Levi who with his famous book's title "Christ stopped at Eboli" referred to the northern- and central-Italian belief that beyond this town, in a southerly direction, lay cultural deserts – that there wasn't any point in going any further into the dangerous southern extremities of this dangling peninsula – parts that were just too alien. Beyond Christian civilisation.

It was this very thinking, among the Fascist authorities in 1935-6, which meant that young Carlo, rather too radical a man for the liking of Mussolini and his stooges, could be deemed to have been exiled – to pose no more threat to Fascism in Italy – simply by dropping him off in this much poorer, yet not really very distant, region of his own country, a mere 200 miles from Rome: Lucania. That was the old name of the modern region of Basilicata – basically ankle-bone to instep on the map.) It's as if a contemporary British dictator, a dominant Mosley, might have thought of exiling too noisy a journalist to Whitehaven. Well, maybe that might have worked, too. And the English version would have been called "Christ stopped at Penrith".

The Northern metropolitan conception of Southern Italy was, and often still is: of backward clannishness; dark villages over black ravines; banditry; mountain-beasts; and finally and worst, the influence of such entities as the *Camorra* (Eboli's just south of Naples), and further south the *Sacra Corona Unita*, the *'Ndragheta*, and the Sicilian *Stidda* and *Mafia*. All of these, to the ignorant non-Italian, are lumped together these days as "the Mafia". In fact locally and within a very large area they are entirely-distinct kinship-societies – though they were all born out of long feudal history, out of alienation, hiddenness taken for inaccessibility, the consequent disdainful neglect of the nation's legislators – and then the fearfulness, negligence and venality of generations of unsupported law-enforcers.

Anyway, here, as far as those in the seats of power were concerned, any civilised creature who had no wish to contract malaria (a serious risk), dysentery or worse should pause, stop, consider and retrace his steps. Here too were known to be bears and wolves, creatures far worse and less edible than the charming wild boar of the Piedmont. Here and southward, no-one would be able or willing to tell the traveller which of these dark people was a mere savage, a superstitious but essentially-stupid native – and who, a scheming, barbarous brigand who might dispense with your ears and tongue while relieving you of your wallet? Clearly, best just not to go there.

Even now, it's still that way, in the back of the Milanese and Roman consciousness. This heel, this instep, this boot-toe all might as well be islands – like the scuffed-leather football called Sicilia, with its troubling proximity to North Africa – parts equally savage, frightening, and to be treated with as much ignorant derision by many of the centralised intelligentsia, as Cleckheaton by Kensington – and worse.

Predictably, the Caravan Club Book, from here onward, will be warning him to increase his vigilance: "around…. Naples … moped riders may attempt to snatch bags from stationary cars at traffic-lights" and "treat with caution offers of help, for example with a flat tyre, particularly on the motorway from Naples to Salerno, as sometimes the tyre will have been punctured deliberately…"

Anyway – and, yes: 223 Squadron did bomb Eboli –

* * *

That the woman in this story is absent, is of her own choosing. (That she's referred to as The Muse, is not.)

She's the one who let him go. She understands that from time to time he needs to. Not that she doesn't accompany him, often, in the van, to the hills, sea-shores, hills and mountaintops, when her work allows it. And in his retirement, how she works!

On his own, through perpetually missing her, he understands he's travelling alone and has chosen to do so. In fact (he muses) she is both Muse, and Joint-Captain. And right now, he'd like her to be here, looking at this map, walking the hill with him, helping him to be clear and *think*.

Joint Captaincy is a very rare arrangement, hard to achieve and sometimes very painful.

And, ah… you see… as it sometimes happens – just now, in Barrea, once again fearful and lonely and about to phone her, before moving on southward (he's made those convincing excuses to himself, but he really won't think why) – At this very moment of need (feels like a very familiar event) – ah – he gets a text message. From her. Phone coverage here, very weak and patchy –

He phones back straight away, gets through third time. Oh, God, there's been a break-in at home. Last night.

Joint Captaincy required that she told him. A rear back window, forced. But, most alarmingly – an unbreathing man, dressed in black. In her bedroom. A blue-white pencil light held low in hand. Picking up her bag. Her screaming, at last finding her voice. Him running. She after him at the front door, barely dressed …

He had to be told … And now, he has to be told, and told again. *He must not come back for this.*

She's all right.

OK, she's *not* all right, but he must *not* come back!

This is obscene, dangerous, to him. Unbearable.

For the best part of this day, walking frantically in circles, he plans, phones their mate Roger the builder about how to re-secure the house, duplicating calls she's already made – but he adds bars to basement windows … unplans, calls her again, now, from Pasetta's campsite office phone because the mobile keeps on cutting out. He outlines new plans: to leave the van in Naples, fly back, arrange something different with Freya, who must now get to the wedding some other way, later. Tells the Muse this.

They scream at one another. He must *not* come back. She is OK, he can tell she is not OK, she says she *will be* OK.

He says he *must* come back, they scream at one another some more.

He shouldn't have phoned again to talk about it, he should just have done it and not said any more, he knows now. And now, typically, the day is nearly past and he still – in every way – doesn't know what he's doing.

Pasetta listens, sad, patient, helpful and the most sympathetic possible – offering absolutely no opinion because he knows *he* can't know either: because he's not the Captain, and he's not the Muse. This is a marriage, a partnership and therefore must sometimes be so strong it's unbearable.

In the end, that night, the Captain sleeps eventually from three to six in the morning. Wakes up. Gets in the driving seat, reverses, leaves an envelope of thanks and the extra night's money through the office door.

Drives.

Chapter 22

In bits – & a self-serving parallel

So. He's not required back. Forbidden. Not before the appointed time. Or she would be someone else. And so would he. On he will go. What he hears in his head now, is a pair of sustained, unbearable notes, held like strings pitched too sharp, and not in harmony, across a continent.

All he can think now is – run, get on *down*. Down, and through Sicilia to Trapani. He's so tired of this journey now, tired already of this nasty, brutish history, tired of soul-searching. Out of emotions. Mad. Irrelevant. Get to Trapani as early as possible – looks as if there's a site on the headland north of there. Quest? Wrecked and anyway, it's still a long way to go to get there, two-and-a-half days' drive even if you did nothing else but drive and didn't even really stop to look at anything – and be waiting there for days... For a plane that still might not even fly!

Solitude worse, much worse, than solitude. The journey he planned, already starting to be funked, he's just pulled it all out from under him. He's a sad, lonely, lost, much older man. This is the Present. And he's heading South. In the wrong place. Again. In spite of the best-laid plans. In the wrong state of mind. At the wrong time.

And *not needed*. That's now the worst thing. Just when he'd started to think it was the best... Horribly familiar.

He reaches a place where the major roads fork for the last time, just south of Napoli and Salerno: final choice for the southbound traveller – heel, or toe?

Whichever way is wrong. Besides, he doesn't know the roads yet. And he's been warned enough about scams and thefts and punctured tyres down here... Look. Get to Trapani. Just hole up there, get sunburned black, try to have a furious, mindless break. Try to stay somehow in touch. The plan, the research, the father-fixation – forget it. Here is a message from the universe: Now. Those towns, those old bombing targets, they're all healed up. Everyone in any case will say, "Just move on. We have". You're on your own, buddy.

Nobody cares, and apparently, now he doesn't either.

Given that he's prohibited from driving back north, or west to Naples Airport... If he took the left hand fork, there'd be no straightforward way back to the toe of the Italian boot. Thus as he continues to the right, towards Messina and the ferry, he'll have made pretty much another irrevocable decision that the inland heights, Italy's southern and eastern instep-and-heel, Brindisi, his dad's targets and airstrips, are not for him this time, either. No thinking. Decision makes itself – it's straight down the toe, to the boat... Exile...

And then: there it is. Eboli, it says at the junction. It only increases his depression to know from Cyril's Log that 223 Squadron bombed Eboli[1] and its environs, in 1943, three times, each plane releasing 1,500 to 2,000lbs of bombs on each visit.

Cyril's new wife, Muriel, with whom he'd enjoyed little married life was far enough, in their northern seaside home, from the risk of all but occasional randomly-jettisoned German bombs. By now, he'd been told, or must have guessed, she was ill. The Captain, indeed his elder siblings even now in their advancing years, know little if anything about how much was known, or was told to him out there. He must have been worried. He must have felt he should be at home. But he still was out here, and not sure that the war would let him get back soon – or ever.

Parallels? Not really. Some sort of counterpoint or fugue. Compared to that, and the place and time, the Captain's situation's utterly trivial. No survivals are at risk here. But in the relative scale of the life he now lives, and the lives among which his emotional life operates – wherever in the world he finds himself – there is a self-reducing irony, all the same. Conflicting duties … But he *isn't bound* to one duty over another. No-one but himself put him on this road, pushing southward still and further away from

---

[1]   See also pp 237-242 to y, below

home; no-one keeps him there. And look here: though the Muse loathes all dutifulness, she's only *Joint*-Captain. Orders from one of equal rank can safely be ignored –

But a whole moment has passed now. In their own places, they both know it.

He hovers mentally, on this Purgatorial borderline. Paestum, west; or east to Eboli? The choice/non-choice is like sampling a bitter taste just long enough to know that if he refuses to swallow fully for now, it's certainly swallowing him. So where the turning is signed Eboli, left from the A30, he turns right – and away towards the coast. Exile? Feels more and more like desertion. Low Moral Fibre?

All the old parallels are finally broken by the fact that now, in his own mind, he's no longer any of those old archetypes – dogged flyer, exiled poet, philosopher, questing knight-at-arms.

Deserter. And did Cyril start to feel that way too?...

… OK. Paestum …

Chapter 23

– Paestum –

Here, this...? Surrealism. This could almost be a warp in Time ...

A German-owned campsite, right on the coast. A camp-site so German and so dated, Lotte feels futuristic.

The aged proprietor, old enough that he needs make no concessions to politeness or international relations, limps glaring out of his flaking gatehouse as if on duty at a checkpoint, and barks "Ein dokument!" without a "bitte". He's gruff, heavy, steely-eyed, bad on his feet. With difficulty our Captain concedes that this old man doesn't look quite old enough to have been part of his father's war. Not... *quite...*

A *very* dated German-style campsite: skirted, hedged, punctuated with tall pine-trees. Each morning, a short crackling amplified burst of Bach-at-the-organ music signals that it is 8am, campers. Early season, still; but the site's fully-open, with beautifully-clean sanitary-blocks, the open-air voids at the entrances to the men's and women's sections giving that particular almost-naturist sense that is so German, so 1930s – or to the Captain so 1960s, so redolent of the dog-eared, monochrome "Health and Efficiency" magazines that were passed clandestinely around his first school-trip abroad, aged fourteen, to Norway. Those were the days...

This, *en plein* air, the Mittel-Europeans have always seemed to suggest, is how the world should be run: and as naturally-comfortable as the Thirties (or the Sixties), this German couple who approach now, older than him but still considerably younger than the proprietor. Both of them loom very large, in circumference compared to height. She is nut-brown, luminous-saggy-bikinied; he's fat-wineskin-paunched, too-briefly-Speedoed, and defiantly-bandy. The levels, already, of their shared tan (by late season, he knows they will be almost black) and their breadths of gut and breast flaunt before them as flags, indicators of wealth. Similarly, their camping-vehicle: immaculate and probably this year's model. How could anyone have driven from anywhere to here – and arrived with immaculately-clean *tyres*?

Of course, in coming here they've all come to be where the sun is – and incidentally it's where an Invasion Beach was, onto which today the lucky campers have direct access through a boundary hedge, the narrow exit-gate locked at night. Last evening there was a remarkable sunset, pink wisps over what must be the dim blue end of the Amalfi peninsula in the distance to the right, and even – black sun-spot on the burning gold horizon – what must be the distant isle of Capri – so famed in song, story and brochure that it seems both incredible and naff to name it.

Should a travel writer digress here upon the subject of Tiberius' pleasure palace over there – or, you may enquire, "Paestum, that also sounds Classical?" – or, upon the quality of the German camp-site pizzas?

The pizza isn't great, but it was a long drive. And pizza is comfort-food.

And OK: yes, as well as featuring a major invasion-beach for Operation Avalanche, Paestum can also boast temples. Greek temples. Huge Greek temples. They are objectively amazing, appallingly intact. They stand by the side of the road down from Battipaglia, where they were unearthed when coastal bogs, full of malarial mosquitoes, were drained in the 19th century.

Today, there's some sort of fair, or massed school concert-gathering beside them and, bizarrely, the entrance is guarded by bouncers, pear-shapes in black suits. The Captain looks across the fence, but in any case it's not a day for visiting to absorb a Hellenic ambience. It's no sort of day for him at all. He tries to close his ears to the din of youngsters arriving, dolled-up, to amplified popperooni musak. He really should make time to go in and look around properly, but come on – he can take his photographs from here, ignoring the unconscious throng, keep them out of the frame and afterwards *pretend* he went round. He means, he can perfectly well see them from here. Truth is, in his current mood especially, they daunt him, these temples. There are several, a – what? – he lacks a collective noun. A laurel-wreath of temples? No, a squat, squared-off *squad* of temples in the drained bog. They actually repel inspection by the likes of him. By being so ancient, so unequalled in complete and generous proportion. No-one can be bothered to build like that any more. No sooner had they become survivors out of their own time, than they must have become hopelessly and forever out-of-place here. It's not surprising they sank, and were left to sink in alluvial slime through the Dark and the Middle ages. Then, rescued entire and intact, he imagines them once again grazed-around by the livestock of nineteenth and twentieth century peasants, occasionally sketched by latter-day Grand Tourists – only to stand still, as backdrop to a 20th-Century armoured invasion that managed just to miss them, and today to host a pop-concert – all of which they simply… overlook.

There they are, magnificent, pristine, in absolutely the wrong place and time – almost embarrassed: large clean ladies caught naked in a field, beautiful to their own self-knowledge and to the gods. It's unimportant that they make him feel uncomfortable. That's it. He'll leave them to it. That's what the Captain does to things now. He's mortified by inadequacy anyway. He can't possibly comment.

Paestum: Temples of Hera/Poseidon 450-460 BCE

The Captain's avoidance of more-than-passing notice of temples has something in common with L/Bdr Milligan's artillery unit as they passed this way, straight off the Salerno invasion beach. Their own Twentieth Century brush with the Classical world deserves quoting:

We reach a secondary road and – here comes the bonus – we pass the Temple of Neptune and Cerene *[sic]* at Paestum, both looking beautiful in the sunlight. Strung from the Doric columns are lines of soldiers' washing. At last they had been put to practical use. If only the ancient Greeks had known …

… I had appealed to Sherwood to drive slowly past the Temples.

"Wot Temples?"

"You'll never get another chance to see them close at hand," I said.

"You're right," he says. "*You'll* never get a chance to see them again," and he drove on.[1]

---

[1]   Spike Milligan: Mussolini – His part in My Downfall Penguin 1980

Chapter 24

Battipaglia – Palmi – southern manners – volcano freaks –
who bear bad tidings – to San Giovanni, rattled

Now more than ever, the Captain is unambitious in the way of cuisine. Coffee, maybe a shower, then awake, jobs done and on the road as fast as possible, heading south before the day's heat here builds up, early May.

Through Battipaglia the minor roads have a local rush-hour, he's found, but even so he's just glad to be rolling, leaving Paestum on a Saturday against that heavy flow of weekender traffic from Salerno, still glad his Dad's mob never (at least intentionally) bombed those temples. But an almost-stationary queue towards him (some of them maybe heading to the temple-fest?) blocks him, vehicles double-stacked across the white line in the jam.

So at the first chance, he's glad to turn out of the coastal strip and away – signed at first towards Eboli again. Yes, 223 Squadron certainly attacked there. And again, very near. There's an Italian account of it that needs to be properly translated, an eye-witness account. Christ certainly stopped short that day.

Once out again on the southbound motorway, the floating, flying feeling he once felt as frictionless escape becomes alarmingly agoraphobic. He's not sure there isn't a deep fault, under one of the stressed fly-overs or under his heart, that will soon send him crashing. And there are peaks still, to his left, with snow atop! Now he knows that even all the way down there, on Sicily, Mount Etna's not going to be a warty little thing like Vesuvius he drove past the other day. Etna's nearly three stacked Ben Nevises.

He stops for just over an hour at a service-station to piss, eat lunch and shut his eyes for ten minutes – waking himself from dodgy half-dreams, and of course on the jump for Caravan Club pirates … Rattled by snakes, not ladders, back to Square One…

He'd never thought he would feel intimidated like this again, just by a road. Repairs, road works, all the way down … In some parts it feels as if, the motorway existing notionally on the map, Italy's government has just now got around to building it … Well ok, that's not fair, but in places it is terribly tattered. And so you can't argue with them renewing the barriers behind these miles of cones, on a carriageway that's mostly constructed on concrete stilts above precipitate mountain gorges. This road must have been a remarkable feat of engineering at the very first.

Now numbered A3, it bumps, crumbles, subsides, closes and reopens its lanes for bulldozers, landslips, the odd incidental boulder and patching of potholes yawning too wide to ignore … all the way down, he's told, from that psychic knot of an Eboli junction to San Giovanni and Reggio di Calabria, and the ferries to Messina. He can well see now, that before a post-War road was parachuted onto this craggy, earthquake-shaken extremity, the metatarsal provinces of Campania, Basilicata and Calabria must have been places of exile indeed.

And exile now, yes.

He's exhausted but grateful, at this day's end, to have made this next step down, into Palmi, Calabria – at the same time desperately playing down the horror that he's deliberately, obediently, travelled further and further from his violated English hearth, home and love.

Shaken in so many ways, he steps down from Lotte this time feeling as if he's just endured the spin-cycle of a badly-balanced wash-load in a Hotpoint missing one of its feet. At least they had the decency on that stretch, not to ask for a toll …

And finds he'll be camped directly above the decent little harbour of Palmi (yes, targeted: August 1943). To look down at this little town, its marina of white yachts, you wouldn't believe there was much point in bombing it. The population even now is only about 20,000. But still – bomb it they did, if only because there was a game going on here that had to be played with the Germans, in odd outposts around harbours on the coast …

It was obvious to the Wehrmacht's commanders that the force landed by Montgomery on the instep around Taranto after their advance through

Sicily would be adequate only to clear that very first sector of the south. The Germans, as they regrouped and left Monty pretty much to it, knew that the major Allied landings had to be made soon, and somewhere on the west coast: mainly by the forces of what had formerly been Patton's[1], and was now Mark Clark's, US 5th Army. The Allies knew they knew. So "targets" on both eastern and western coasts were regularly but randomly to be "softened up" from the air in order that Kesselring could be kept guessing.

The Captain's grateful he can find no information as to casualties from his Dad's boys visit. He hopes most of the bombs ended up in the sea. Then he looks it up in the Log. Ah. They set off in thick cloud, and among several others that day, Jack's navigation failed to make their required rendezvous with other aircraft, and they turned back. However, Cy had to note under "remarks" that "five other formations attacked at 10 minute intervals". That must have been more than a stone of bomb per head of population, as a purely-diversionary tactic.

And who's to say that this cliff-side wasn't eroded into its present broken shape less by wind and weather, more by TNT? This caravan-site is hidden in a quiet pine-copse: on a sloping, rather crumbly little cliff above the sun-blue Med. The land's colours are the dark-red, rich brown of pine-bark and needle-drop, with sharp green explosions of spring-new needles. He's taken serene-looking photographs from a rustic-railed edge – a startling, high-contrast view through the trees down to the marina. In the sixty-seven years intervening, there's been plenty of time for all of this landslip and vegetation to have moved back in, smoothing things over: red-brown, citrus-green scar-tissue; and the perfect, blue Mediterranean wrinkling her pretty little nose indifferently as ever.

---

[1]   Patton had been removed from command in Sicily after reports emerged of him striking two shell-shocked GIs in a field hospital for showing "cowardice". He was back in time for D-Day.

Moreover he knows it's going to be uncomfortable to show these all-too-pretty photographs later, to the main person he might expect to want to show them to. He can't think about that. And will *their* landscape heal?

This is a necessary stopover. But he continues to feel like an abject, voyeuristic fool. He's coming to the conclusion that it's – just because he is.

He feels diminished in another way by the disregard which the Palmi campsite-owner here hides only half-heartedly from foreign patrons. This too is a game played by both sides and as such a traveller himself he tries to discount it. There are teeth on show in both directions, so let's call them, with holiday optimism, smiles.

He learned a lot about middle-and-southern Italy from Pasetta: certainly he understands the contempt of the tough mountain-man for politicians, governments and bad news of all kinds. Now, for the deep-southerners. If there's always a contrast between the two Frances, north and south, and between the two Britains, even the two Englands, he's not been surprised to discover that the two halves (for a start) of Italy are regarded by their inhabitants as distinct territories. He's yet to find out if Sicily will be yet another – and therefore regarded as no better than a poor province of a poor province of...

Anyway, he can't help but notice that these Calabrians maintain (a step-change from contactful Pasetta) sheer off-handedness in the face of those whose mobility shows they have wealth beyond reach. These guys would prefer not to have you here, really, Captain. In order to make their living, it's admittedly necessary, but they'd really rather it weren't.

The site-manager knows that his own countrymen, except perhaps the occasional pair of tent-toting youths on bikes, won't often call upon his facilities. But the idle rich from the north (not of Italy, they aren't actually to be seen here at all) but from northern Europe – Britain, Netherlands, Germany, Switzerland – will pass through on their sun-seeking way south to the Sicilian ferries. The camp-site owner will accept their money, naturally, it pays the bills. He won't overcharge, not for food, drink, staying, anything. But he won't pretend this trade of his is one for which he has very much taste. The cupboard from which he serves– bar, kitchen, "mini-market" – isn't very well-stocked. He'll neither be happy when someone like the Captain makes an appearance, nor sad when he leaves. There'll always be someone, maybe not so many, but someone, just passing through, please God.

Far more meaningful to *him*, one can see, are the visits of tradesmen or his friends from town: his own folks, just popping in as much to pass time as anything. Together they'll enjoy themselves grandly, laugh and shout; then, in a few minutes the proprietor'll stand, hands under his apron regretfully, as their little van or car or moped goes bumping off up round the track and back down into the town, out of his reach again.

These are undecorated, spare communities. Everyone keeps a good deal to themselves, shares in Family and pays some dues, irregularly, out in… taxes? To whoever. Above all they aren't people who would have to travel many miles and burn many litres of fuel, like tourists, to find one or two precious accidental people of the same mind, or to "find themselves". Here, they're saying, see: this is us. Who are you, and why should we really bother with you? … But there is actually no reason to tell us.

What you see is what you get. What the Captain got here is a site that had been hard to find; barely had roads, just worn ochre tracks through rugged trunks and pine-straw, dusty sloped pitches; a lot of sun for a good part of the year; shade from it when you want; aggressive mozzies on the tops of the open toilet-block walls, meebling in your ear and round a bare bulb last thing at night; a great framed view of the sea and of a foreshore into which this site will one day inevitably slide, out of cloudburst, earthquake or gradual erosion; rickety electrical posts into which you can connect your rig with a bit of a fizz; a bottle-bar; a five-tabled pizza cafe.

It's a place to rest for a night, or maybe two if you're tired and demoralised, on the way down to Sicilia or back to your world, Tourist. The proprietor's indifference continues to be total as he shows those teeth and pours you another small beer. His business, his contentment for now, doesn't depend upon customer relations. You'll either come back or you won't – it won't be soon anyway, and it's more than his self-respect is worth to show much respect to people who don't even know who they are, and never will.

For the Captain, well, that's really how it is too, especially when he looks in the mirror. More than ever he can only be the ghost-captain of his one-man ship, skipper of his own wheeled and waiting plane from another age. He starts to hope these few days will soon have become little more than roads of Forgetting.

Lonely and low as he is he's instantly glad over pizza, to meet a sociable couple who happen to be English. Christine and Simon. They realise now, they did actually glimpse each other, or at least each other's vans, back at Paestum. Simon's recently been given early retirement from a university job in Wales: "Yes, a few of us were taken out one day and shot."

They're actually on a volcano-tour! They're heading south, like him, have already done Vesuvius twice: just three days ago, and once years ago. Tomorrow, like him, they're off to Sicily. Obviously. Etna first. Then Stromboli, off the coast, and there's a couple more volcanic islands, too! They're excited. Every year, you see, they go off somewhere different, just for the buzz, for the smoke and the lava. Last year they holidayed in Iceland.

And hohoho! They're glad they've *driven* down *here* this time, not flown! This ash-cloud now has got planes grounded *again, right across Europe!*

Oh? Had he not heard?

Oh God – he explains his mission, meeting Freya's plane and how an entire wedding in Sorrento depends on clear skies, as first the happy couple, then other guests, will arrive in penny-numbers, their flights scattered through next week, the second week of May. Do these vulcanologists think everyone'll make it? "Oh, well, maybe, no problem I hope. So long as ... Oh yes, I should think so, probably – there's a few days yet – and look, don't worry. At least *you'll* get a good holiday out of it! Ha ha!"

Yeah. And now he shouldn't, but typically and too easily tells them about the burglary back home. They go a bit quiet and exchange looks.

Next morning: Road of forgetting. Road of flight. Road on stilts. Road on cliffs. Road above, or bypassing, habitation or comfort. Road in tunnels as if, on a plane, you close your eyes a few seconds in a spot of turbulence ...

Roadworks less frequent, but still present; because, so far down, they haven't yet even *begun* on repairing these twisted, rusting barriers. The road's still the same aging concretion, strung over gorges.

Another temporary deliberate forgetting: that the whole of this, this A3 south to the toe, is strung on an active earthquake zone ... With breathtaking views! So that he can imagine, scarcely breathing, how easily Lotte and he could end up as a tiny dust plume in the bottom of what he's just glanced at, through the crushed gaps, over the edges on his right. Hold the road. And how useless are road-signs that warn of falling rocks? Completely. On the road itself is plentiful evidence: fallen debris, some recent enough. He keeps his eyes on the slabbed, patched carriageways, Lotte clenches her teeth, weaves a little round a boulder, straddles a minor flake, mud-brick, pothole.

Eventually, he has to laugh aloud at a sign: "Scilla 2km". What next? "Charybdis Welcomes Careless Drivers"?

Then suddenly – if anything *can* be sudden after an hour of cursing and cold sweat – *it feels suddenly*, he's down into San Giovanni – suddenly there are cluttered road-signs so vital that they are double Dutch to the anxious driver who has had nothing to read for hours – but then, even more suddenly, huge, marquee-sized (thank God) signs that scream TOURIST! FERRY OVER HERE!! ENGLISH PLONKER!!! CAN'T YOU BLOODY WELL READ??? or at least, he feels, the implied equivalent, in stencil-lettered Italian a foot high. So now he follows the turns to BIGLIETTERIA…. Head still pounding, he parks quietly and turns off Lotte's engine and a nice man who looks like a little balding Tuareg in a petrol-advertising tee-shirt, with only one tooth in his entire mouth, and who has seen *many* tourists with this sort of distraught, silly stare down here, talks to him soothingly as if to a child, translating for him to the very cool ticket-office guy who could perfectly well speak English himself probably, then he asks for a nice tip maybe for his kind help and is disappointed that it's so little, but anyway tells him how to proceed from here and actually, although it's a trip of less than a hundred yards, it's a good job he does so, because there are no road-signs again or lane markings on this built-up corner, but the Captain has now learned he must make a left turn at a tiny unmarked junction across busy traffic where he would never have turned if he hadn't been told, and now he's obviously There, near the *other* ticket-office and that's just for foot-passengers, but then he must turn Lotte back on herself onto the opposite side of the jetty and the ferry-boat is waiting for him, her mouth open in front like a whaler (or a whale) disgorging its last gobbets of folk from the other side of the Strait, and then he's rolling Lotte in, and over and up, and they're in, and now he's upstairs taking more useless photographs of nothing much, seagulls in smoke-haze – and the ferry's working its mundane repeated way towards the other side, leaving him drunk and slightly seasick, but from the hardness of the land he's just left…

The road still buckets and rattles in his head over the racket of a crowded boat. His ears still clatter with Lotte's surge on the ill-fitting slabs of concrete and with the bang, bang, bang of her hard, hot tyres on metal expansion-joints.

Part Five

Sicilia May 2010

PRODUCER *(to the Stage-Manager)*: Jesus! Get them out of here! …

THE FATHER: … I'm astonished! Why don't you believe me? … Perhaps it's because we're not in the script?

THE STEP-DAUGHTER: *(coming down to the PRODUCER, smiling and persuasive)* Believe me sir, we're really six of the most interesting characters. But we've been neglected.

Luigi Pirandello – Six Characters in Search of an Author

Chapter 25

Messina – low-flying – Finale puzzles – unwell – the Muse – dreams &
distortions – and on again – Father, Mother – unreliable oxygen –
humility v daft hats

In what feels like mere meaningless moments more, they're into Messina.
That means there's now yet another stretch of water between him and her.
Him and home.

Is it because it's the start of a sleepy, mezzogiorno afternoon? Maybe. Is
he in some sort of shock? Probably. But – are the road-signs here not newer,
cleaner, calmer? Aren't the streets themselves, and then the roads, simpler,
broader than those back on the mainland? Is this because Messina is a sort of
suburb to sprawling, proud Catania? Has his mind been washed into some
sort of quiet again for a moment by blue, flat water, by bright white gulls
floating across a mist-recessed Mount Etna as they would across Whitby
Abbey, the sea-level breeze rinsing through what remains of his hair?

Yes, probably all this is true, he reckons, as Lotte spirals gently upward, her
patient gears winching them up the hillside: out of town again; onto another
Autostrada. They pause at a *servizio*, and elect to turn north. He admits a
tentative sense of achievement at just having crossed that water, at having
driven that far, at being able to say he has reached Sicily, which a month ago
on the map had seemed an exciting but scarcely-feasible prospect.

He's very tired – tired of driving – but it feels so much easier, here,
than back on the mainland that he continues for now, automatic as Lotte.
Too tired even to think about Etna – except to remember that Simon and
Christine reckoned they'd be off up there tomorrow – he heads for the top
right-hand corner of the island (plenty of shipping in view offshore, no
obvious whirlpools or grasping tentacles). Now the road hangs left along

the northern coast, in the general direction first of Palermo, and ultimately Trapani. Only 200 miles … The views of hills, and of Etna now dropping behind, bays and bights of sea approaching and receding to his right … these then have been his first views of Sicilia …Green, blue …Above all, yes, a better, easier, much newer road.

It occurs to him as he calms gradually, that even here the carriageway has barely touched ground since he left the port. Though his low-flying is no longer over ravines, but just above treetop-height over patches of agricultural land, alternating olive-groves, vines and fruit-plantations, he's still not *in* the countryside; but encouraged to continue gliding *over* it.

Now: if you landed on Mars, and put up at the space station – to research an entry for 'The Hitch-hiker's Guide to Campsites of The Solar System' – thinks the Captain (somewhat deranged) – you might find yourself noting down, "The most striking thing about Mars is the oxygen-pumping apparatus, which is much quieter than anything on the Moon". But he hopes you might also get around to drawing attention to the particular quality of the red earth, and the sense of the planet's actual gravity (not just the artificial stuff at the Mars Hilton). The business of getting there, as a jobbing journo-naut, might well have been arduous; OK, but eventually you're expected to step out there and get some reddle on your boots, sample a crater or canal, view an ice-cap and a sunset – or you might as well have stayed back on the moon, and just sent home the little-green-martian-cartoon postcards you bought in Caffe Luna.

That's what he's been doing recently, the Captain senses. Circling on concrete clouds, *over* real, inhabited places. Absorbed in diesel prices, campsite pitches, old war-traumas, and above all his own internal strife. He most despairs of himself when he finds himself behaving like this as he travels. All right – he is a little spaced-out, admittedly, in a kind of fixed panic, but the only point of this travel is exploration. He must make up for past negligence: look hard this place, not hurtle over it in some sort of blinkered, panicky-tourist bombing-run. You have to connect your feet eventually to where you are. With a fixed wedding day ahead to attend, speeding through here won't get him home any faster. He must *try* not to be wasteful.

He dives off at last, down towards the sea, to where the Book tells him there's a campsite. The name of the town, Finale. A good place to stop.

As he takes the turn and drops, the weather turns dull, a little misty – it even looks like rain? He finds a small, scruffy-bushed bay and a primrose-yellow concrete site with a pleasingly North African-sounding name. A rotund, self-satisfied boss is standing at the gate in a crumpled suit, green braces stretching over shirt, beyond open jacket. Bald, operatically-welcoming and in a blink, dismissive, he shakes the Captain's hand through the open side-window and motions him into the Office where his sensitively-featured, tragically-intelligent daughter will do the paperwork. She directs him onto "our second street", a raised concrete apron overlooking a rocky slope to "Street One" which is right above the sea, and where he'd rather be. But he finds himself not solid enough to request anything better than what he's given.

Parked up, he's glad to walk a kilometre back to the little town. Only one shop is open but it sells most things he'll need.

Here, he begins to feel a little odd, but in different way. Or really the place itself is a little odd? It's a typical dusty southern main-strip; but many of the more modern properties here seem to be empty, like a run-down village street on a Sunday afternoon in County Mayo but with street-dust baked cream-yellow. Most of the businesses look as though they should be active, he thinks, now that it's evening, but in fact more are closed and shuttered than open.

There are some folks dotted about the main street. A woman of middle age or older stands alone, sentinel between doorway and gate, and looks sidelong over the camouflage-purpose of her yard-broom. Men are much more in evidence, and in groups: for instance, five young men, next to a boy on a Lambretta; a slightly larger group – of fathers, you might say – smoking near the petrol-station that's an island-outpost in the middle of the broad main way; and four elderly men, raising and turning heads in mumbling rumination of his arrival, where they're seated on the low wall outside the shop where he passes them to buy his groceries. Not many people, and not very animated. Watchful.

And now … No, he wouldn't *exactly* say, these people are staring at him. He *has been* stared at in his time: for instance a couple of years ago in Huesca, Basque-country northern Spain (near where George Orwell got himself wounded in the Civil War) he and the Muse had frankly been goggled at in amazement, for the whole of one exploratory day. So he knows what that feels like – not entirely comfortable, but you get used to it. Not that he expected to be received by the shopkeepers here with the careful deference evinced in the shops of Castel di Sangro – only a week, but so many kilometres, ago.

No, and here the reception is worse than Palmi: he looks to people, and they actually glance away – his Buongiorno freezes on his lips. His Ciao on leaving the shop is made to seem an absurdly flippant remark. He can catch no-one's eye, and yet he knows no-one's eye is off him, until he's passed the town sign again and well off on his way back to Lotte and the campsite. It feels they can see through him. Maybe they can see he deserves to be shunned.

What's more, now there's definitely something wrong with the weather. Whereas on the southern toe particularly at sea-level it had been bright, warm, close to pushing his too-hot button – and before that up in the mountains, of an evening it had frankly turned chilly – here on this coast it's grey, muggy, restless: as if a storm's brewing. Back at the van on site as evening draws down into night a torpid climatic unease continues, and worsens. Blocks of air like warm cotton-wool, and smelling like grey bathwater, move about in the trees, but almost silently, with at the most a whispering gasp, while seeming determined to bend some of the palmery in half. From inside, it feels Lotte's being humped and shifted about by a team of camouflage-grey workmen who pick up a corner of her in trial, shift a bit, rock and throw her back down – but without any of the loud drama that would explicably accompany for instance a highland gale or an alpine cloudburst.

This will continue all night – and then subside, if only out of weariness. Then rain falls fairly hard for five minutes only, at 7.30a.m., prompt.

This, he imagines, may be Sirocco? Research indicates that all winds in the Med have their special names. In Libya, where this one begins, it's called Ghibli. The cement-like taste and smell in the atmosphere is North African desert dust. Once he works this out, he's rather pleased he's got it from direct experience, rather than some travel-rep's explanation.

Ok – but now what about explaining his reception in *town* last night? He feels now he was getting the social equivalent of this meteorological unsettlement, or as if his arrival there had stirred up something dark, grey and restless among the natives. Then (of course, as he dresses for the new day) it becomes clearer, simply bathetic. A man more given to physical rather than internal expression would have smitten himself heavily on the brow. "Wah!"

"Shorts!"

That was very probably at least part of the reason. This is after all Sicilia, southernmost of Europe – why, barely Europe at all in some ways: almost Africa. So just because you got heated-up as you drove down, you fool, you had absolutely no business hitting a respectable little township in short trousers. Now he knows he's just been an ignorant yob, and has quite understandably been seen for what he was.

Right. Now he'll be able to interact with Finale in a different way. Properly-dressed, over the next couple of days he'll go back and do some shopping, taking respectful photographs of the more notable buildings. There's a derelict factory at the exit of town, half-demolished between the road and the sea. It matches the mood. He photographs it. Finale – is just what it is and is prepared to show you. It has no readable history. It's remote from his life. So he safely takes pictures of bright spring flowers too: monumental bushes of scarlet pelargonium, and a pink-trumpeted convolvulus whose ambition is to take over the world. There are statuesque thistles and a flaming jacaranda cracking out through the concrete grounds of the dead factory – in front of the black, broken windows, twisted ramps and rusted pulleys.

And it turns out that today in the shops, they're happy to help him choose his sliced sausage and his bread, they tolerate his schoolboy-Italian from CD and phrasebook. And well, actually if you had seen his knees the other day, maybe you wouldn't have known where to look, and would have been willing him to take them back out of town as soon as possible too.

Personally and socially then, a better couple of days. He actually finds himself chuckling rather madly at one point. Not that the weather has changed. He's uncomfortable in his bed, stripped to nothing and jolted rather than rocked by sirocco. Then he is sweating profusely; then really starting to feel wrong, ill.

Perhaps it was something he ate. Or maybe it's sand-fly fever, such as had attacked Milligan on the mainland? Or malaria from the drained swamps? 223 Squadron started to collect loads of that. Those mozzies in the shower-blocks at Paestum, Palmi. Or maybe the other day they gave him something bad in the shop, the smiling witches, because of the insult of his knees?

But it means now that he must sit still, in a clammy fog, sweat, shiver and starve selectively; anyway all he has to feed himself on are mobile texts and a phone call with the Muse, who still sounds crazed and undermined by the burglary – to which has now been added a plumbing disaster causing a flood. In this context, trying to describe mild fever and a few digestive symptoms can have no place, and he doesn't attempt it.

Somehow everything has come together to symbolise all that is wrong, for her, with their relationship. He says: when something material goes wrong, it's generally because of external circumstances. To her (she *is* a psychotherapist) problems are always failures of communication or of relationship, writ large into the world.

Look, he says, it's horrible – I know – but shit does often *just happen*.

Oh, I can't be *philosophical* like you, she says, you just won't let me be *emotional*. Which is true: but when she yells at him as if he were an idiot, the devil, or even the very burglar or incompetent plumber himself, it scrambles his brain. To him, women are capable of doing the most unbearably-painful things. Her long-distance distress is now the most terrible thing he's felt since another woman he once knew, periodically crippled by depression, started actually bashing her head against a wall. As he fought to stop her, everything he ever knew about a benevolent universe had started to balloon off into oblivion.

But where is *he* in all this? Does she have a point? Does something in *him, make* all this happen? He's built his own ramparts against it, over many years. He tries gently to bolster, to extend them. Look, he says, really bad things have happened back there and maybe I *should* have just come home, *whatever* you said. But to talk about it right now, can't we at least start at: I'm OK, you're OK? It's a vague sort-of-therapeutic mantra he once heard and he desperately wants any formulation to have a bit of shared currency now.

Oh, she says, *you're* OK. *I'm not OK.* And of course, anyway, he's not OK either.

There's another couple of days' non-communication after this. He thinks he's being strong, but the bug he's caught gives him shed-loads of nasty dreams. In one,

> *children on skates are practicing for competition, on ice so thin you see the water bubbling below. A little five-year-old in blue sequins – it's Laura! – steps out, stands on the ice – and falls through it with a snap. Everyone stupidly laughs, but in the dream he sees: she is shocked, lifeless, drowning in this blow-hole. If he can stand astride, as though he has no weight, and reach down between firmly-planted feet, maybe he can pull her up out of the water … and – yes – he does it!*

He likes to think of himself rescuing children. Wakes up smiling. Drifts off again …

> *At After School Club, he's collecting Laura. The assertive black woman who is in charge this evening says disapprovingly that she understands he normally has nothing to do with his daughters, who live with their mother. He's furious, since both in this dream and in former reality, both opposites are true. But elder sister Emma, sitting by, says nothing to contradict it.*

You can check out any time you like, but you can never leave … your past, your paranoias. It's become part of this house he drives around in, the home he carries on his back.

He'd better move on, ill or not. He has to break these bad spells, out-speed the vulture again.

He packs up, battens down his cupboards, unplugs his mains, and taxis tediously, shivering, around the site's quasi-airfield-concrete to the gatehouse. Here he notices again how a line of two Dutch and four German motorhomes have monopolised the best row of Street One pitches immediately facing the sea – and for the first time he spots a Belgian campervan next to a French in a sulky corner next to a cement-heap. At the site-office, he pays what feels like a lot of money, as required by the pretty young daughter. She tells him again in answer to his question, that the factory on the edge of town closed many years ago. She won't elaborate except that it is sad. The old man, the *padrone*, is again in position outside on the road admiring his yellow, bougainvillea-encrusted walls, one thumb in waistband, the other caressing his comfortable shirtfront, a damp stub of cigar in the corner of his mouth. Again and forever, he'll be talking to everyone passing, arriving, leaving; and stylishly takes the Captain's hand in farewell, as he did a couple of days ago in greeting. It's prosperous charm, impersonally-applied. The Sicilian *paterfamilias,* doing his thing.

Lotte points westward again, on, along the northern coastline route towards Palermo, and he tries not to look back in her mirrors – at Finale, at Mount Etna, or at the mountainous foot of Italy. He doesn't want to look back at all any more, or to have to try to sleep again in that still, dodgy breeze. He's not well, shoulders shrugging and shaking intermittently, pursued by hungry ghosts: a Fury in a telephone, a bride on thin ice, a nightmare of lies believed.

He needs to make sense, driving almost, but not quite, towards his farthest point. Rolling westward along Sicilia's northern coast.

Farther, Father.

To meet his father? No, his daughter.

Fathers. He is a father. And here's the whole question – of fathers, and what they do just by happening to be in that role; what he, as father, continues to ask of, or owe to his children; what Cyril, so long gone, continues to exert by way of duties and guilts. Our father who art in heaven …

His dad, after his Methodist upbringing, had led a life which contained enough tragedy, war and disappointment to leave him, if he had ever been anything else, no stronger than agnostic in the matter of belief.

Once, in the late '60s, an occasion had arisen – from Cyril's weary humouring of his own old mother in her complacent expectation when her time came, of a vaguely-Heavenly Methodist Realm to float off into, replete with sofas and cups of tea. Asked by his son (at the callow age when such questions, if ever, will be asked) he'd explained reluctantly that his view of an after-life was simply: that you live on, if you do at all, in people's memory. It had seemed at the time to the youth that he'd personally, by angry, persistent debate, *forced* his old man into this formulation. Now, he thinks this dad's reply to that badgering adolescent was respectfully-honest and considered.

But suddenly it had seemed to leave horribly-open the next, troublesome, universal question: what would be left to show that he had *ever been here at all*? Whether or not it ever kept Cyril awake, it troubled his son. What was the answer? Some very old black-and-white photographs, most of them fading – and one small colour print in a frame in a drawer. In twenty years' time, who'll be looking at those albums?

Lasting achievements? A scrapbook of pocket-cartoons published in the local newspaper; some of his drawings, framed only after his passing, of local landscapes.

Other scraps perhaps passed on; some words recorded in mouldering Minutes, of the town debating society or his spell of parent-governorship at his sons' grammar school. The activity for a while of that little local ATC "squadron".

Ownership of the little terraced house he'd left to his widow and which ultimately would be sold to pay for her care. A log book; and – "the tape".

All pretty ephemeral. What would his dad's answer have been to that? He would simply have said, his children. Children – and his grandchildren, and so on. Offspring. But would he even *recognise* now, if he returned with his eyes and wits still about him, this particular, grizzled son? The grand-daughters he once blearily lap-dandled, women now of-age? The one he never lived to see? They would all have to reintroduce themselves; and then the old feller might find a strange selection of his own characteristics gradually begin to reappear out of a bunch of strange new adult faces: emerging odd resemblances, or recollections of nose and grin, Cheshire Cat-wise. And he might even notice some quaint family phrases, old jokes still in use …

His "Memory", though. As a man, as a presence? Even less defined, and yet where does it stop? 'Caesar dead and turned to clay might stop a hole', certainly. Yorick certainly lacked jest upon exhumation, but lived boisterously in the Prince's memory all the same – and has been alive ever since, for millions to whom he is neither more nor less than an illustrative master-sketch. Living in the memory's a tricky business, tricky to track, tricky to verify, supported on other folks' unreliable oxygen.

The truth is, the Captain muses, a lot of what's left of his father is bone-memory. A whiff of paraffin, Swarfega, fag-ash, awakens it. How much of his own occasional elbows-out strut-walk is learned imitation, and how much genetic? Close to the apex of a challenging ascent, he'll find himself leaning forward over Lotte's wheel and dashboard to encourage the last drops of momentum, his head toward the windscreen, just as the old man sometimes did near the very top of "Hackness Hairpins" in his work-van on the family's Sunday afternoon ramble for blackberries, trying to throw them all, his family, microscopically further-forward onto that "ockerd" little summit as bottom gear was applied and the clutch burnt and screaming, and Mum twittered, "Should we all get out?"

No point discriminating nature from nurture, when mirrored reflexes are so strangely enduring.

It *was* good of the Old Man to answer so frankly on the matter of after-life, given his diffidence in any matter of absolutes too close-to-the-bone. Because yes, there was always that sort of tact, on the part of both parents.

They would both generally withhold themselves from expressing strong opinions. Their reticent post-War liberalism steered along cautious paths of Maybes and Perhapses, and always between extremes. They kept at a careful distance, between those grouse-moor Tories and Bevanite Socialists; between the comforting notion of a loving God, and the reality of two Wars' meaningless slaughter; and finally between the sampler-text that children should always respect their elders, and the sense that these booming babies must hold – would need to hold – most of the answers for the future in their own precious, precocious, newly-educated heads.

Politically always hopeful, his dad loved most to see, (on BBC 'Panorama' interviews, say) post-colonial leaders in Africa – Hastings Banda, Nyerere, Kaunda – who were wily enough to sound both well-educated and respectfully liberal, as if just for him. A particular favourite was Singapore's Lee Kuan Yew. So well-spoken you had to believe he was certainly no longer a communist; such a kind face and quiet cultured voice you could not believe he could be tyrannical. Cyril wanted a world of fairness and equality where bygones could be bygones and former underdogs would in turn be selflessly grateful for, and inspired to goodness by, the coloniser's enlightened granting of their independence. After all, he had had no part in their former oppression. He was much more in the Methodist missionary camp. Well OK, he *had* once been photographed with a kudu he'd shot on a plantation-visit in Kenya – and once, his "boy" under canvas in the desert *had* been beaten, presumably by others, for stealing a pair of trousers. But that's just how things were back then, he'd have said.

These parents knew they couldn't glorify war, even one won to overcome Evil – and actually understood they shouldn't imagine, either, that their experience of its horrors or of anything else in Twentieth-Century history entitled them to pontificate to kids who, All Being Well, would live on into an unimaginable Twenty-First. They had, above all, that genuine and remarkable humility – remarkable to the extent that it often infuriated the very offspring it was intended to potentiate, though they wouldn't have used that word.

Nowadays it's fashionable, smart even, to say of such humble people, "They have a lot to be humble about." Ha, ha. And wasn't it Nelson Mandela who said:

> Our deepest fear is not that we are inadequate. Our deepest fear is that we are powerful beyond measure. It is our light, not our darkness that most frightens us. We ask ourselves, Who am I to be brilliant, gorgeous, talented, and fabulous? Actually, who are you *not* to be? You are a child of God. Your playing small does not serve the world. There is nothing enlightened about shrinking so that other people will not feel insecure around you. We are all meant to shine, as children do. We were born to make manifest the glory of God that is within us. It is not just in some of us; it is in everyone and as we let our own light shine, we unconsciously give others permission to do the same. As we are liberated from our own fear, our presence automatically liberates others.[1]

There is of course great truth in this, but if it had been pronounced in their own lifetimes, it would not have occurred to a close-to-bankrupt ironmonger or his wife in a coastal town in 1960s Yorkshire as having a lot of bearing upon *their* lives. They didn't "shrink", he surmises, out of cowardliness. They didn't "play small". Simply, they *were* small, and they knew it.

---

[1]   Well, most people who have seen this quotation know that this came from Mandela's inauguration speech in 1994 – and the fact that they know *wrongly* is an interesting example of the synergy that is possible between fame and humility. The quotation is actually from Marianne Williamson. She's not strong on humility in the usual way, and is in fact an activist for, among other things, peace, and women's rights in the USA. Williamson says she's now happy that the quotation has attached itself to Mandela, realising that her words have gained much more currency through that association: she's pleased to see the benefit of the words being spread, and *humble* enough not to need the credit so badly that it's worth her getting worked up about; this, even when her words as a feminist writer have been stolen and then given away again by men, first to an iconic man, and then to be spouted in at least two Hollywood blockbusters in muck-or-nettles moments by alpha-male sporting coaches to their gumshield-chomping charges.

They were self-effacing. He imagines his father taking out a chunky lump of eraser and with a light sigh setting to work to expunge a dapper self-portrait.

Nowadays everyone is by comparison inflated-big, bigged-up, needs to be noticed, Deserves it, is Worth it, is Entitled to it. That's maybe what his dad saw coming, and wanted toned down in *him*! His parents didn't feel the need of any of that. They'd dress up in their best when they went out together; a couple of times a year. But it would be out of respect for the occasion – at a local school, theatre or chapel, mostly – and certainly not in order to *shine*.

In fact – ha hah, yes, very likely anyway – his father, if he looked back at the War and that whole era, probably felt that most of the evils visited on the world by Hitler, Mussolini, Stalin and subsequent tyrants were simply caused by their *lack of consideration for others*, and their want of proper humility of spirit.

If so, the Captain thinks, the old man probably had a point.

Dictators? Too big for their boots.

Writers? Self-important fellers in daft hats, said Cyril.

Robert Graves, for instance

Chapter 26

San Vito – Ustica – reading matter – levellers – roll-call – disappearing –red
sky at night

In one final lurch, an example of Lotte's best, almost driverless road-holding, this afternoon he has rolled into the bright, luxurious expanse of a campsite on the very north-western top corner of Sicily. The drive that brought him here was a horrible hot yomp which took him through the very centre of Palermo, an experience he immediately promised himself never to repeat; on through a string of dry townlets that begin to remind him, in their cream-gold evening dust, of Morocco. Onward, outward, and curiously this last few days westward, to this pre-determined stop: several days early for picking up Freya on the 7th from Trapani, a mere forty kilometres southward down that ultimate, western coast.

There's a huge blue pool, there are monumental flowering cacti landscaped into the corners of white-paved terraces, there are invitingly-empty ranks of red sunbeds, red sunshades. It's still early season, the first week of May. There's a pizza restaurant (of course), lots of local information, and a hut for connecting to the internet.

He knew all along, since even before he set off from home, how much he'd appreciate this arrival. It stands for the farthest-flung outpost of the trip, and the conquest of a tough three-thousand-plus kilometres. It is arrival, too, in the airfield-land of his father – in a way that makes a meeting-place for their stories which will now travel together in the same direction for a while, across this island and back up into southern Italy.

It's perfect in its own way, even luxurious, in fact the very, sun-loving site as he'd selected in advance, from its description in The Book, the place he'd most want to be able to bring Freya, straight off her flight. But well … It's a good job he's here in good time … and that she's not here yet… because … it's not just the heat … depressed, lonely, still feeling sick, the Captain's waking life is much less real than his dreams, in which former teachers and work-colleagues have started to visit him impromptu, dressed up as motley troubadours or masked motivational gurus. Motivation? How he needs it.

A dulled-feeling illness: dozing … and waking fitfully to a crazed sense that he and the Muse may never speak to each other again. He thinks of her: at night, insecure in their creaky old house. He thinks of her here, in his van, when he needs her conversation. But when last he heard from her, he felt she could do better without him.

Walking the camp, drinking his coffee, eating his food, reading his books by the pool-side, dozing, still much too white, floating in swim-shorts which balloon absurdly in the glittering water, he tries to occupy himself, rest, even do a little writing … but by the evening of each day he's very low.

The sun on his second night sets apocalyptically upon the shark-fin point of yet another exile-prison of the Fascist era, the distant isle of Ustica – Antonio Gramsci was imprisoned over there in the 1920s.

Disquiet, increased by choice of reading. At one hand he has William Least-Heat Moon[1]. The thing is: wherever *he* travelled, across byways of the USA, Moon had *conversations*, and far more of them even than those which in Steinbeck's "Travels" would be edited up into set-pieces. Moon's work is packed with close observations of the places, and particularly the people, he happens upon. He's a real celebrator of the folks of the US back-roads. Admittedly, he shares with those he meets both a language and some sort of homespun cultural reference. Indigenous, his is a book warmed throughout by honest meetings, connections. It makes this particular lonely reader, perversely, lonelier just now. It contrasts too heavily with the depletion of his contacts since he left Pasetta, up in the mountains of Abruzzo … He feels that more than ever as a personal shortcoming, even though he'd prefer to think that the implosion of his morale and the fact of inadequate language excuse it.

And – always reading more than one book at a time, on his other side is Rilke: The Duino Elegies (in translation of course); itself by turns, exhilarating and disorientating …

---

[1]   William Least-Heat Moon.1982. *Blue Highways*. Little, Brown & Company

"Why [would one]want to exchange a child's wise not-understanding for
defensiveness and contempt, when not-understanding means being alone,
while defensiveness and contempt mean participation in that from which
one is trying, by their means, to separate oneself?" [2]

… For Gods sake get over yourselves, he finds himself ranting, raving under
his breath, at a certain category of campervan drivers, other ships' captains!

They're away, on holiday, right? Camping, allegedly. And yet there's the
same compulsion, as if they were still at home in that suburb, or as if they
were still driving the company car, to stress their conformity to acceptable
standards of appearance. Here at the ends of the earth, it feels, they must still
be seen doing the Right Thing, and doing it perfectly.

Here, says the Captain, we're under bushy little pines and olive-trees in
the north-west corner of Sicily. And yer man and his missus, who happen
just now to be German but in this matter might just as well be English and
in England, are on the pitch just up the rise and across from Lotte. (She lolls
in a relaxed sort of way, handbrake and parking-gear fully-engaged, laterally
across the slight incline that rolls to the end of the site and after that to a
dark-blue Med). These plonkers also own a Hymer, but of course larger and
much more modern than Lotte – and what has he done? He has jacked up

---

2   Rilke: Briefe an einen jungen Dichter 31-32 tr. J.B.Leishman Norton Library edition
1963

his van, on the lower side, on jack-legs; and then additionally placed wedges under his wheels; in order to "level" his home. Why?

The Captain has seen this done on almost every campsite on which he's ever parked, which was not absolutely billiard-table-level – and in fact, on some that were. The transformation, it seems, from rolling "motor" to static "home" must be achieved totally, incontrovertibly. Otherwise – what? The toilet will overflow on the floor? Er, no. The kitchen-sink or washbasin won't drain? Yes, they will. Your satellite telly (for God's sake why don't you just stay at home?) won't work? Of course it will. Rupert Murdoch is flying over us as we speak, in his Sky-rocket, ensuring it. Perhaps without the precaution you've taken, my friend, your games of carpet bowls won't work, your putting-practice might be ruined? No, just made more unpredictable.

What does this allow them to do, that they otherwise couldn't? This levelling-up? Well, it enables them to pretend they're not on a slope, even the slightest. The floors at home are level, my dear, thank the Lord, and so they shall be here. I won't have you worrying your pretty little head about that. (Don't shake the lettuce out of the door, for goodness' sake. All you need to do is plug in the centrifugal salad-washer.) Oh, and have you noticed, look – I've put the spirit-level on the dashboard, and both ways – look – perfect!

Lovely, dear. Well done! Bikkits?

Grrrrrrrr.

This practice also enables these men to have conversations with drivers of the same nationality – serious, chin-stroking conversations – about levelling, and about levelling-equipment, levelling-technology, and the relative merits of different pitches, on this site and others they have known. During these conversations they mock-discreetly avert their gazes over each others' shoulder, shaking their heads to mutter in lowered tones that of course they have noticed "the man over there who has not levelled his rig". It could be an H. M. Bateman cartoon.

Even a Caravan Club Book chap would no doubt say, Well it's always best to be safe, old man; supposing your brake failed (And my gearbox, simultaneously?) and that old bus of yours rolled off and killed some little tot …

Bollocks.

This Is Camping. When was the last time you saw a *tent*, pitched on a slight slope, and raised at one end for the insertion of an inflatable wedge-shaped flooring system? Oh, because otherwise the pan wouldn't quite sit flat on the primus, would it, and our sleeping-bags might roll together in the night, dear, and then what might happen?

Thus, the Captain's *sotto voce* rant as he smacks his mats against a low wall. Ach. That's enough. But he's prepared to bet some newer vans do already have a built-in electronic dashboard spirit-level.

Then of course he learns: it's already an iPhone app.

On the third morning of his attempted convalescence (for that's the only way to configure this early arrival) he starts to take notice of a hi-top van which pulled up just below him the evening before. It's German; more a conversion-job than a motor-home; newer than the Captain's, a contrasting dark blue. The side facing Lotte is a blank, van-metal wall behind the two front windows. He's only seen one occupant – and there he is again, he's heading for the toilets. Haha! Up before he was! But of course he probably drove a long way to get here yesterday. And he's exactly another Captain, with grizzled chin but shorter hair! Luminous green t-shirt, blue shorts, desert boots; fit-looking yet with that slightly-uncertain, groping gait he knows well from getting started in the mornings, at that age, on uneven ground in a strange place. Now he's back, in a changed, blue t-shirt …

And now, of course, he's talking to someone else in there. Yes, there is a woman's low voice … A like-minded individual, then, judging by carriage and vehicle; but not, as our Captain finds he had hoped, another solitary …

Feverish still, he starts to feel his familiar self disappearing, as if that were only a figment of his own dream. At the same time he *feels* as if, to others, he's ultra-visible: spooky grey-bearded man who might be up to no good, standoffish at best; at worst … Then he's angry – as with the levelling tribe. Never mind about why *he* doesn't talk much to *them* – why don't *they* talk to *him*?

He should learn German. Then he could talk to them – and, incidentally, read Rilke in the original. Maybe he'll be alone now for the rest of his life, so there'll be time. It's not too late. Once this wedding is done – it's another step towards his own enforced, belated independence.

He hasn't ever felt able fully to let go of those girls. But Emma's a grand success: despite the recent collapse of that Bank, she'll always be on her feet, with her smashing feller and now a baby on the way. Laura: so proud of her

– so determined, so funny; definition of the efficient social worker; and very soon now to be wed – to a calm, quiet young man. And Freya, at nineteen – flying out here soon, volcanoes permitting – once he would have been desperate to ensure she could be stimulated, occupied – it would have felt to be his serious responsibility to entertain her; but now, may it even be the case that *she's* humouring *him*? – playing along in his quaint old rambling adventure *as if* …

Ah. Thinking of them, as always, calms him for a moment. They are, at least in part, his achievement. No doubt all three dear young women will always just find him odd, eccentric Dad, from now on. He just doesn't know any more how he's seen by almost *anyone*. And now, even the Muse … The one and only Muse …

He remembers: "Oh, *you're* OK. *I'm not OK*" – and feels the keen doubleness of that edge. Although that conversation was later, he feels he was told not to rush to rush home to her because she sees *him* as complacently *OK* in himself, so he simply won't be of any use to her in her emotional vulnerability, her post-trauma state. But: for her to say *he's OK*! He'll always know that he wasn't there with her, when it happened – to stop it happening – and *still* isn't there *now* –

He must seem, to her, to not understand nor *care* enough. But then if he *had* absolutely shown it, gone straight home – that would probably have been no use …

Suddenly it's all about how he's seen: he's shrunk. To the Muse, to the girls, even to these caravanners … And right now, unable to speak to any of them.

He finds himself repeating an old, old mantra from what feels like another life.

He has to be OK.

He decides it must be that he's deliberately isolated himself, in order to understand … that he is an isolated man. Deliberately? He knows, actually, he's often been a different, rather lost sort of person. He tried for a long time – when the kids were younger and advances in salary to be earned – to create the *conventional* shell of identity for himself; but he's no more capable of forcing himself into that now, than he ever was – or of flying to the moon. Taking that leaving-gift, that retirement, he'd thought at last he could leave behind that suit and start afresh, that maybe it was true that he was always meant just to be a free molecule, a man in a van, a scholar-gypsy. No more shell required than that.

But without a *shared* identity, he's now found he becomes motionless, motiveless. Blue clouds have blown through him, sometimes to his exhilaration, too often a rude gale between the ribs, carrying bone-dust from mountain-towns; ashes from the far north. Without a self-appointed role, he'd have no shape at all. All that's left of him is a vestige, at the end of one little tip of Europe, on his own, in a van. A speck.

For this moment, even Lotte doesn't contain or shield him. He feels – for one long moment – as if *he's* starting to be blown away, like his dad, his mum, in ash. His eyes cling onto the rising white sunlight as it climbs the trunks of the cold pines. He keeps a tight grip on that mug of tepid coffee and fights to prevent his focus sliding away into blur, into personal cloud that's dark and dangerous. He could just … sit here now and not-be. Not let the sun rouse him. Be found like the skeleton of a pirate on Treasure Island. Skull and bones. Faded clothes. Staring out of black sockets and with no interest any more in brushing off the flies …

Evening. He's been trying again to read, or write – eating a tired salad – and is roused from his torpor by a couple of sharp little screams from seaward. He steps out of the van and up onto the otherwise-deserted terrace, to see that the screams are from a young woman, in co-ordinating white pedalo-slacks and sweater. With her back to the most amazing sunset yet, she's yelling to her feller, who's fighting with his camera: he has to get her, you see, here, on the wall, her and the sunset and the wine-dark sea, quick, before it goes – the sun! And he does, he gets it, gets the picture. Look, look … Yes!

The Captain's so grateful to the pair of them – for pulling him outdoors now, tonight. He did take his own sunset-shots last night; but this tonight is an even *better* burning pink, and more widespread on the long, low ribbons of horizon. And as if to demonstrate a solar system exactly in *progressive* action, the burning orange ball has shifted over just a little to the right from the other night – so it's now fallen, not perfectly atop, but slightly off, the sharp little black hook of Ustica[3] … Off the hook …

Well done, you two! And thank you. If there are any Shepherds about, they're Delighted. You and the red sky are suddenly a fitting Delight to this proverbial Englishman. And the proverb presages something no worse – even, maybe, better – tomorrow than today.

---

[3]   Wrong again, Capt. – it was Levanzo, to WSW of San Vito. Ustica is to the N.

Yes, he *has* to be OK. He'll just do as he's told. She says, Don't come back, I don't want to hear unless you can tell me something joyous. He won't be back yet anyway, and there's nothing he *can* tell her, except it's a good site, and Freya will soon be with him, and he's already told her that.

Youth, oh, youth!

And yes, yes, yes – Freya soon *will* be with him! And soon after that he'll be doing as he's told by Laura, the bride-to-be, who has organised her event in such a way that there will be no option but for the father of the bride to follow instructions … And Emma will be there to keep him steady. And meanwhile, he'll just do as it seems he's told by his fellow campers, too – continue to keep himself to himself. But keep making eye-contact with them whenever possible, as he has been doing – and do his best to smile.

He'll do what the Young world tells him, from now on in. That's safest. Across fifty-eight years, he's stretched from a childhood in mid-twentieth-century England into adult life, Love, work and Strife, and now into a strange no-place called: Taking Stock. Soon enough reeling-back-in from all that will begin. Everything will re-boot again from Trapani. He'll start to be back with his daughters, in their hands and under their gaze – and though far-flung, that'll mean he'll *feel* at home.

And anyway, why feel so strange? Where are all these other campers driving to? These captains and their mates? Why, only out – and back. All of the outward trips represented here, like his, were originally for their notional destinations. Yet the real destination is always Back. Home. The safety-net of all recreational travellers. If nothing else, in our beginning must be our end. And in our end, a beginning – Most journeys must return full circle. It's an old story. And always in the storied Quest, it must always be that he will return Home – and it must be that in some fundamental way he will be Changed.

There's going to be a Wedding, for goodness' sake!

Which may turn out a rite of passage for the father, as much as for the bride.

Chapter 27

223 Squadron, Tunisia – Pantelleria – Trapani – attempted infiltration of nuptials – Invasion of Sicily – 223 to Malta – and a new sort of target

Since the beginning of summer 1943 in North Africa, thanks to successful interdiction of Axis supplies by submarines and aircraft based at Malta, 223 Squadron had enjoyed – though they wouldn't have thought so – a relatively flak-free time of it. Now the Desert Fox was driven away, their next Ops would be over the Med.

They were called in to bomb – repeatedly – the tiny volcanic garrison-island of Pantelleria: on the 6th, 8th, 9th, 10th and 11th of May, from Fauconnerie, Tunisia; then again, from Enfidha, on the 6th, 8th, 10th and 11th of June. Cyril at some point filched some aerial-reconnaissance snaps – marked Secret – that showed German and Italian aircraft destroyed on the ground, airfields and huge underground hangars rendered useless. Eventually, on the 12th of June, Pantelleria became the first garrisoned military territory in world warfare to be forced into surrender by aerial bombardment alone.

By July 1943, 223 and 55 Squadrons had already bombed Trapani, their first Sicilian target, from Reyville, near Tunis:

Raids on Trapani would reduce enemy chances of moving reinforcements from Gardinia where [it was known that] the enemy assumed that the invasion would take place …

… [9th July] Baltimore FA298 was attacked by an Me 109 and was seen to dive steeply into the sea 15 miles from the town of Trapani. No-one was seen to bale out, and no movement of dinghies was seen after the aircraft crashed.[1]

---

[1]   Extracts here and below from "Wings defend Africa – The History of 223 Squadron Royal Air Force 1918-1963" A. Butterworth, F.L.A. 1988. Apparently based on Squadron Record: unpublished Draft typescript now in present author's possession.

Cyril logs the same events:

9.7.43 0940

Trapani Milo   Baltimore IIIa 342   Ops22 as briefed Flt Sgt Connell

Two boxes of 6, led by Flt Sgt Brown, following 55 Sqdn. Escort 24 Warhawks
to each sqdn. A/a fire very heavy, concentrated and accurate. Sustained attacks
by E/A – 109s & Reggianis. 4 e/a shot down by combined action of fighters
and bombers. 223 Sq bombing good. Load 4 x 500lbs 1 x 250lbs. Losses one
bomber from each sqdn & 2 fighters. We had one hole.

INVASION OF SICILY STARTED NIGHT OF 9th/10th

What a word, now, thinks the Captain, to read on actual road-signs! "Trapani"
will be doubly revolved on the tongue: once for this; and once at least for
Cy who – though understandably in the circumstances he never expressed a
nostalgia for any part of Italy as longingly as he did for the beauties of Kenya
– nonetheless savoured the foreign sounds of Italian names, as a sense that
he could hold them as inhabited places, familiar towns, down whose street
… well, somehow as names of old friends, old enemies, old excitements.
Cy's post-war pronunciations emphasised the exoticism over the context.

Cyril and his masters of war stressed it Trap-AHni. In Italian, the stress is
actually on the first syllable.

Other lives will keep tripping on his heels, though: at 7.30 this morning a text message has pinged in – from Mike and Maggie.

Oh, please …

They're "still near Florence" but, Mike's finger-taps add, "wondering about the weather further south" because now "it's not very nice" there and they've been "thinking of going to Naples" …

The Captain bridles: Naples?! First he imagines that enormous rig of theirs gridlocking the whole city in a cacophony of Lambretta-horns.

But mainly he knows now for a certainty what they're trying to do in heading that far south. They're trying to horn in – of course – on the wedding in Sorrento. Now: they had been invited, months back, along with a number of other friends to a separate, big Reception, scheduled back in Leeds a week or more after the main event; but they'd sent their apologies for *that*, long ago – sorry but they'd still be *away* …

How irritating! Then, typically – "oh, anything for a quiet life" – he starts to allow himself to – well, still, he supposes, if they turn up at the wedding, maybe that could be OK …

No, no! – He's furious, as he now tells his mobile screen in no uncertain terms. He wouldn't dream of trying to do the same thing to them, or to anyone else. And anyway, this is *Laura's* event! There's a very limited guest list. Even some of her close relatives don't figure on it! But he finds himself clueless how to reply. This bloody message of theirs – now – sent at the crack of dawn – inconsiderate on the one hand – pretty barmy on the other. Mike is being as usual both indirect and tiresome, trying to guilt-trip him into an obligingly "spontaneous" invitation: "Oh, Mike, great. Well hey, what a great coincidence! Why don't you drop round? Sure, matey, of course we can fit you in!"

Ptcha. As if. There's more than enough to hold in his mind, without including Mike. He won't for the moment reply at all … See if they get the message from that…

… Chicken …

On the 10th July, in 'Operation Husky', Montgomery's Eighth Army landed at Gela on the southern coast, and Patton's US 5th further west at Licata.

Eleven days later 223 Squadron transferred again – they had moved airfield once a month since April – from Reyville, to Luqa on the island of

Malta, less than a hundred miles south of the landing beaches. Malta had been beleaguered for two years or more. In 1941, the last Allied stronghold on North African and Mediterranean supply routes, its defences at one stage reduced to just two serviceable Hurricane fighters, it had been one of the most intensively bombed targets, over time, of the entire war. Yet unlike Pantelleria, the island had remained undefeated, and its inhabitants were famously to be awarded the George Cross.

The 20th of July saw the last of the major Axis air-attacks on the fortress island. 223 Squadron, it was noted, found Malta's anti-aircaft barrage "impressive". Now before them was the next land over which Bob Connell's crew, in their full-sized version of a boy's later plastic Airfix Martin Baltimore Mk IIIA, would fly their next sequence of Ops, dropping their two-penn'orth into the mix: from Malta, further into Sicily, to rip holes in airfields and disrupt troop movements by road.

223 Squadron fuelling and loading up for a sortie from Luqa, Malta,
July 1943

But this was also the next phase of their war in another respect. Now, they were also bombing *towns*. Through late July and the first week of August they would bomb – in some cases more than once – Adrano, Troina, Mistabianco, Regalbuto, Paterno, Centuripe, Randazzo – as well as "enemy concentrations" and gun positions across eastern Sicily.

Tomorrow, the Captain will pick up his youngest daughter from Trapani airport, and together in the next ten days they'll retrace his steps – back up that big boot – to Sorrento.

174

Chapter 28

*Trapani, airports – waiting – wondering –a navigator at last – ... to
Agrigento – the art of parking pointedly – a haunted beach – civilised disdain
– the art of pointed departure – and a puzzle*

TRAH-pani. After that shortish drive, (through a real town called Purgatorio)
this counts as his end-point. From here, everything will be Return.

Trapani, Gerbini, Catania, Brindisi, Foggia – back in 1943 they'd been
straightforwardly enemy airfields to wreck, capture, patch up again and re-
use; and (except for Gerbini) airport-towns are what, unsurprisingly, they
remain today. Even so, this son of Cyril, who has in more recent times visited
many a far-flung, semi-rural Ryanair-pitch that's barely more than a flying-
club with a bus-stop, finds it a real facer that Trapani Airport, on the outer
limits of an outer limit, is now graced by an international facade almost
as imposing as Arsenal FC's new Emirates Stadium in north London. This
evening its terminal looms, a block of mirror-tinted glass uncompromising
as *omerta*, up into another all-new Sicilian sunset.

He's arrived so early, of course, partly out of excitement, and partly in
trepidation that in his present mental state he could easily have got confused
and lost the way. Security-guards loll about, armed, uniformed, immaculate,
chain-smoking. The car-park is long, narrow, high-fenced, pretty full. Lotte,
not without experience of such tight spots, nonetheless edges her way
gingerly through the barrier-gate, finding she needs seriously to hitch her
skirts in and limbo her high-domed forehead under a striped iron crossbar.
Behind the wheel, he's peering upward, edging, wincing. Only... just.

He really has now reached his furthest reach, through a gateway again
that brings to mind camels and needles: after a reversing-manoeuvre into
a parking-space he'd have rejected anywhere else, at any other time, as too

narrow, he's drenched in sweat and stress; but now, finally at rest. Very early indeed.

Will this flight of Freya's really be on time? The arrivals-board suggests so. But it's a question with a basis in real concerns: because in the UK and all points north there is mounting anxiety for the coming days. Ash *has* remained well-and-truly in the air, as he's been updated regularly in texts from the bride-to-be and both her sisters. Widespread flight-disruptions may well prevent them, and/or other guests from crossing European airspace in the planned flight-slots. Even with redirected or rescheduled flights they may not make it, even at all, not before the wedding! His own drive back up from here to the Bay of Naples may prove comparatively ancient and plodding, as befits his age and his vehicle's era – but if he can keep relying on Lotte's rattling cruise, she will have made an arrival more certain than a state-of-the-art Airbus. The tortoise and the hare … But now – will the whole event be able to happen at all?

More immediately, will Freya's flight really get through tonight? – she said by SMS she thought there was no problem with her departure … He goes through into the terminal and checks out the Arrivals screen, *again*. Expected on time. But he's still very early to meet her, so strolls back, draws Lotte's blinds down, undresses, towels off, buffs himself up, puts on clean clothes including the designer t-shirt Freya bought him last year from her Oxfam fashion-show, sits and drinks his coffee and begins to wait out the couple of hours for her mid-evening arrival.

* * *

That night, back at San Vito after midnight, but well-practiced from previous trips, she makes a contented tent out of the big bed that can lower, like magic, from the ceiling over the front seats, and the floor-length curtains that separate off the front of the bus as *her* domain. There she'll doze, and read, as long as she's allowed, most mornings now until they reach the wedding-hotel.

* * *

Next morning, now, before Freya's out of bed, he has his rituals to perform to demonstrate responsibility, dispel anxieties and propitiate gods. He unlocks Lotte's bonnet to check yet again and top-up minutely the engine-oil, the radiator. All that was well-serviced before they left, and he's kept it up pretty obsessively, but any breakdown (mechanical *or* mental) at this point in the expedition couldn't possibly be afforded. He recalls what she solemnly reminded him on arrival last night: they have just ten days in which to get themselves up (in his case, back) to Campania: Sorrento.

Plenty of time, of course. All planned. And there's also plenty he wanted to fit in before then. Not least: conversation, sun, sand between the toes, the joy of stitching out a journey together with the beloved girl, queen of the maps. Pizza … pasta … ciabatta …; Agrigento, Villa Romana, Etna; various bombing-targets in Sicily; then, on the mainland, for speed, convenience and the-devil-you-know, necessarily Palmi again, and Paestum. And – Eboli? Only after that route can the bride-and-bridesmaids-trio of sisters – fingers crossed – be reunited in Sorrento. And … But …Surely in the meantime, his dad's war-sites aren't a fair imposition on a nineteen-year-old needing her short final break from vacation-cleaning-jobs before starting at university?

Soon, after spending another day or two basting at San Vito, by the blue pool, on the red loungers, among the monumental cacti, taking sun-drenched photographs and laughing at each other, they're heading off. Now no longer alone, his passing through Purgatorio becomes unambiguously a laughing-matter. The hill-town of Erice glitters; and passes behind; and they drive, drive off through hills and scrub, and south for Agrigento.

There isn't much conversation, or need for it. On his right, the navigator has the map on her knee, a Japanese manga paperback on top of that, and her iPod plugged into her ears. Both she and her dad are contented, grinning. Lotte hums along in German, up and around winding roads, down remote defiles. The roads are pretty ropey, B-to-C-standard, but the Captain's in his element. They're on rather a detour, in fact, and without any WW2 justification, to the furthest southerly point of the trip. Most importantly, in his head though, they're definitely on the way Back.

Arriving into south-coast Agrigento, they're distracted simultaneously by the return of the silvery Med, out of sight for a few hours, and a distant view of honey-coloured Greek temples up on another hill – so that at first they miss a turning. But soon enough (Navigator shifts effortlessly from road-maps to Caravan-Club Book) they roll down a ridged concrete ramp between dusty buildings, below a down-at-heel corner of town, and into the beach-side van-site.

He cruises in very gently, to minimise dust. There are five or six other vans dotted about, and a couple of decent-looking spaces. He's not sure which to pick. Oh, but there are three in a row, empty behind him, he spots in his mirror, and starts to select Reverse …

Twenty yards away to their right, reading magazines or maybe maps outside their modern German-registered wagon, sits a couple, perhaps ten years older than him. Freya's opened the window on her side. Reverse …

The man barks something at them.

"Sorry?"

"*TURN … OFF … MOTTOR!*"

Freya looks at the Captain. The Captain looks at Freya. They shake their heads in mute, goggling disbelief. We've only just arrived! We've not even parked up yet! Studiously then, and to furious glares, he selects neutral again and carefully pretends once again to consider his options. Then slowly and with precision he reverses twenty yards, to within six inches of his chosen electric point, looks again in both mirrors, smiles graciously at their new neighbours now thirty yards away and … bowing slightly from his Captain's chair … turns off his motor.

This site's proprietor is absolutely the most uninterested and unhelpful of the entire trip so far. Well – after all he can't be the proprietor: Serb? Croat? He's just a watchman really … No language to which the Captain has access, will access him. There are dark looks, almost a snap of the fingers for the passport, the money in advance; and a gesture with two fingers which represents his understanding of the number of nights they'll stay. The Captain immediately decides to reduce that to one finger.

They walk back past two more German vans, through a gap in a roughly-straightened sand-dune, for the beach. The sun's already low, and this is neither an Invasion- nor a bathing-beach. It's covered in litter, crap, jetsam. They make the most of it by walking east, up to a dilapidated, but not very long-established villa, then back a mile or so westward, to what looks like a run-down cafe or coastguard station raised up on the scrub a hundred yards inland. It's boarded-up.

Then they start to take surrealist photographs of the beach, which is all there seems to do: of strange plants growing out of the sand, their shadows enlarged grotesquely by the lowering sun; and bits of fading, degrading bits of plastic, including particularly what seems a black galosh. Are these the

careless discards of campers; or remains of landings, or wreckings, of small North African boats? He's uneasy, saying nothing.

Then they go back to Lotte. To read; to sleep; to dream …

As they say goodnight and turn in – the tiny isle of Pantelleria, only forty miles from Tunisia and sixty from Trapani, is subject to new encirclement and incursion. Like neighbouring Lampedusa to its south-east, the island has become a staging post for leaky, overcrowded craft – African and Arab emigrants, mostly lone males, on desperate journeys north in the boats of traffickers who've taken all they own as the price of a ticket.

The Italian Navy has sporadically, during 2010, been "assisting" Colonel Gaddafi by returning these refugees, to his increasingly-overcrowded Libyan camps. More often, of course, boats will capsize or get swamped. Then bodies are washed ashore, on news-television or for instance, on Lampedusa's tourist beaches. It's a long-standing reality, strenuously ignored by everyone who's at a comfortable distance. Apparently another favourite route from North Africa northward to Europe and prosperity is via Malta … And onward, all these routes, via Sicily. Numbers of escapees, and consequently numbers of deaths in transit, have at least doubled between 2007 and this year of 2010….

One such overcrowded craft has recently been spotted, drifting and disabled in mid-Med – known-about, watched, internationally, for two weeks – no national authority wishing to take responsibility – and as a consequence of civilised disdain sixty-three people have perished.

He wakes up from a dream in which he's asking his dad, at the gates of the Valley of Temples: "D'you think the GIs'll mind, Dad?"

Now he wonders why his dreaming self thought Cyril would *know* how the GIs felt. And about what? This visit? Anyway his dad wouldn't care about *them*. He used to have more contempt for brash Americans he'd come across ("Yanks wearin' great big cowboy-pistols in planes stuck all over with guns an' carryin' biscuit-tins full of bombs!") than his son would later have for ... owners of excessively-large motor-homes. But it feels this dream is telling him about his craven unworthiness – softer-times, baby-boomer fake-Captain – on a half-hearted, barely-apologetic ramble past signposts in a wartime logbook; and yesterday, on a modern beach dumbly pleading for attention.

He returns from his morning visit to the grimy shower-and-toilet block, mentally listing his jobs in preparing to move quickly onward; only to be faced with a column of seven modern German vans. Drawn up from all previously-invisible corners of this small site, they're queued up and blocking the only exit, which is next to Herr Turnhoff-Mottor's vehicle. A group of immaculately-beige-clad adults aged from thirty-five to seventy has gathered, all clustered around Herr and Frau T-M, and his big map. He appears literally to be lecturing them on the day ahead.

And please note, Captain. *All* the motors of their empty, waiting vehicles, are running!

It seems to the Captain that he's seen more Germans in the south of Italy, and on Sicily, in campervans – oh yes, and that one old guy running a camp-site – at Paestum – than representatives of any other nationality. Of course, Italy is marginally handier for Germany than it is for England, and the Germans are great campers. But this lot seem sterner, more intent, than those he's met further north. Again, he refuses the obvious absurdity that *these* might be old enough to be contemporaries of his father's. But – like him – sons? Well, chronologically, that seems plausible. And grandchildren? Doing their own tours of battlefields, invasion beaches, In Memoriam?

(But no, surely. Agrigento, unlike Paestum later in 1943, wasn't actually an invasion beach. Quite soon, Axis forces were driven back into the town by the US 7th Army, who had landed down the coast between Gela and Licata. But by all accounts it had been defended, with a stoutness which earned unwilling respect from the invaders, by the *Italian* Army's Tactical Unit Chiusa Sciafani.)

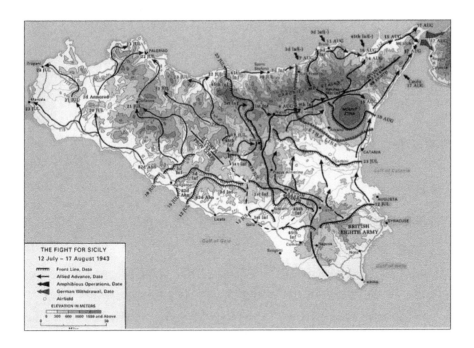

THE FIGHT FOR SICILY
12 July – 17 August 1943

Front Line, Date
Allied Advance, Date
Amphibious Operations, Date
German Withdrawal, Date
Airfield
ELEVATION IN METERS
0   300   600   1000   1500 and Above
30

Thoughtfully he spoons his coffee. He wants to understand what he's witnessing, but before he can ask – the kettle takes a while to boil – Herr T-M and his partner have folded voluminous charts and climbed back aboard their rig. The whole crocodile of heavy, subordinate vehicles now backs up to allow the leader to manoeuvre … Then, with much exhaust and dust, T-M leads them in stately process up, off the ramp, away, up the hill. What's to be made of this? Did Herr T-M instruct his cohort to repay the English interlopers in their own carbon-currency? Or is he no more capable of spotting the plank in his own eye, than of irony? Do Germans really lack a sense of humour? Not in his previous experience, at least. Why is it that the Captain must fantasise that these folks, too, are visiting World War Two places? He can't shake off this probable delusion. Rationally, it's far more likely they're visiting Classical sites. Nonetheless, they've departed with all the stern efficiency of an armoured column.

Chapter 29

Skipping tourist-spots – Pirandello – Fascism in a nutshell – Freya is polite

As soon as the dust has settled, Freya and the Captain strike camp too. Having left Purgatorio behind yesterday, they're now very close to Kaos.

The modernist playwright Luigi Pirandello was born in Kaos, a village just outside Girgenti (Sicilian for Agrigento) and his house, much smartened-up and museum-ised, is still there – and open to the public ... Sometimes. Not today. And the Captain and his daughter continue straight onward, as if it were still yesterday. Freya's plugged into her sound-system. The maps are again on her knee. They pass, at a greater than interested viewing-distance, the temples of Agrigentum; they draw her no more than him. She's relieved too, probably, that the Casa Pirandello is closed. Anyway, they're conscious of needing to drive purposefully, and so they do.

He feels remiss, guilty to have missed the eminent ruins – which, in fact, they'll never even approach. Not that the GIs'll mind. As for the great dramatist ...

While Samuel Beckett might have been just the man, last evening, for a dialogue between a plastic galosh and a half-eaten spade-handle up to their necks in sand, Pirandello would surely have won the literary election to demonstrate that the Captain and Herr Turnhoff-Mottor have themselves been playing roles whose stage-directions were composed long ago and elsewhere.

It was Pirandello, between the Wars, whose dramas taught the world that whatever we find we're saying, is only what's been given us to say. In his world no-one really has autonomous power. If they try to grasp it, they'll only prove that they've lost the plot, and must learn: either they're not themselves at all, and unwittingly cast; or left forever stuck in Limbo – Kaos maybe – as "Characters In Search Of An Author".

In 1934, twenty-eight years before Steinbeck, Pirandello won the Nobel Prize for Literature. It's perhaps unfortunate (and certainly more uncomfortable for the Captain than the earlier examination of Giorgi Morandi's life) that as far as anyone can make out he was solidly Fascist throughout his adult life. But he was first and foremost a Sicilian, born in 1867, and he had come to a sort of fascism as a very young man, through his association with a native, Sicilian movement quite different from the twentieth century party of Mussolini.

The Sicilian *fasci* of the last thirty years of the 19th Century, it is said, rate an honourable mention in the history – actually – of *Socialism*.[1] A movement with striking similarities to Michael Davitt's Irish Land League of the same period, they started a principled struggle against ages-deep oppression under Sicily's absentee feudal landlords. Their ideologues came out of the University of Palermo, where the young Pirandello was roughly their contemporary. They termed their cadres *fasci* – meaning "bunch", "league", "union" or "unit", depending on how you feel about groups of people who band together to stand up for their rights.

So the struggle of the original socialist *fasci* against old reaction, though it was eventually put down, set out a new way – through sustained, unified stands against the arms-length power of old barons.

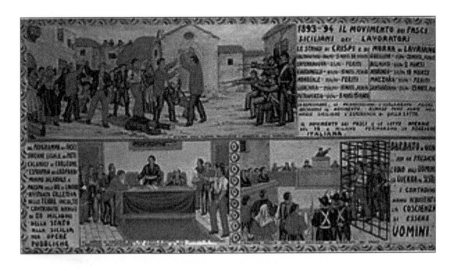

---

[1]   According to Eric Hobsbawm: 1959 *Primitive Rebels* Manchester University Press

A contemporary map showing some bits of "Italia Irredenta":
e.g. Monaco, Dalmatia, Ticino, Malta

It was in attempted emulation of this Sicilian movement, that a later wave of socialist groupings, before and during the Great War, in Milan and Turin, would begin calling themselves *fasci,*. Maybe it had just become a cool word. When later, in the 1920s' bitter aftermath,[2] all of Italy's nascent political forces were stirred up, the Fascists of former-Socialist Mussolini rose out of the pack.

D'Annunzio, narcissistic nationalist playwright, had destabilised things, playing up the injustice of the Versailles (St Germain) treaties, creating and re-establishing territorial claims for various bits of the Mediterranean and

---

[2]   On entering World War I, by the Treaty of London in 1915, Italy had been promised considerable expansion down the Adriatic coast. However Italy was marginalised at Versailles and these promised gains were not substantiated.

Adriatic (e.g. Fiume[3]) as rightly Italian – "Italia Irredenta" – lands now "owed back", in return for her War-sacrifice.[4] A number of eye-catching nationalist provocations proved that Mussolini, a newspaper man, knew how to exploit the populist press.

Yes, he absolutely showed Hitler how to do it. Even while wearing spats. (The man to his immediate left (or in picture, to the right) is not the young Spike Milligan. He is Italo Balbo – later to become first, a legendary peacetime aviator; later still, wartime Air Marshal. Based on one of his strategies, a bomber-force combining a number of separate squadrons was always referred to, even by the Allies, as a "Balbo Raid". He was killed during the Desert War when his plane was shot down over Tobruk. The British, bearing in mind his pre-War exploits, treated his remains with what they felt was due honour.

---

[3]   Now Rijeka, Croatia. During this adventure, d'Annunzio was the first figure to promote the "Roman" salute (no evidence of any genuine *ancient* provenance) – after first seeing it in Giovanni Pastrone's colossal epic film *Cabiria* (1914) for which he had written the screenplay. The gesture was soon adopted by the Fascist Party and then of course most strikingly by Nazism. However, it should be noted this was also very similar to the "Olympic salute" of the time (see posters for Paris, 1924); and (before it was replaced by hand-on-heart in 1942) the Salute to the Flag performed every morning by all US schoolchildren. .

[4]   Among states composing the WWI "Entente", Italy had actually suffered a higher percentage of military casualties, compared to national population than, for instance, Britain.

And by now, Mussolini was leader of the Nationalist (first) and Socialist (second) Fascist Party. A famous but largely-mythical March On Rome followed. This was a stunt organised by others, including Italo Balbo, and opposed by Benito until the last minute (when he arrived by train). But all the instability and hysteria was by now much too much for the King, who was terrified by what had seemed likely (under "liberal democracy") to become a total breakdown of law and order. Result: in 1925 Mussolini was handed the Premiership.

This allowed him swiftly to confer upon himself whatever dictatorial powers he wanted; by which time a large proportion of the population (though never a democratic majority) were pleased to have found in him a long-dreamed-of 'strong leader': and thus, *Il Duce,* for eighteen years to be Italy's dictator. Which is what "Fascist" has meant ever since.

After World War II, when the troops of all those countries returned home again, *actual* Socialism, or something very close to it, initially would triumph in several countries, including at the UK's landmark General Election of 1945 ...

But everyone knows Socialism in Europe these days is a dead duck. It was sunk under the ruins of the Berlin Wall, drowned in flooded mine-shafts, poisoned by the taint of Stalinism, crushed under the floors of empty factories gutted of their heavy machinery – and finally rendered meaningless where "there is no such thing as Society". These days, globalisation promotes below-subsistence pay in Asia and Africa and begrudges welfare to the "undeserving" at home, while at the same time exalting Freedom of Choice for wealthy, deserving or not.... erm... "stakeholders".

He thinks it's ironic that in recent times, although 'Fascism was defeated' – and its name, along with 'Nazi', turned to rarely-exhumed abuse – and all its emblems, in their various national forms, outlawed ... the leader of Italy for at least eight of the last twenty years has been a charismatic and unscrupulous newspaper boss from the north (does that CV ring any bells?) Silvio Berlusconi: whose party, *Forza Italia,* now in 2010 is supported in office by *Liga Nord,* a strongly right-wing party which opposes immigration and champions Italy's "Christian identity" and "Judaeo-Christian heritage" to fig-leaf its xenophobia.

And again, if 'Fascism was defeated': what's to be said of the military dictatorships and one-party states which form the majority of the national administrations of the world? Fascism, of course, being unthinkable without aggressive nationalist policies, swaggering macho leaders … Are these, he asks himself, globally on the decrease?

The present danger of Fascism is the fact of its actual ubiquity, but under other names or guises. Fascism *in name* won't return widely to respectability or power any time soon. But a policy or world-view can call itself anything it likes, yet remain *at heart* fascist: primitive, Alpha-male, survivalist, populist-nationalist, anti-immigrant, hooked on violence or threat, dreams of conquest, lottery-economics, spectacular shows, bread and circuses. Fascism, he reckons, remains absolutely a continuous thread in twenty-first century life. Always ready to become the next new thing, always under its next new name.

The Captain and his daughter now almost stop to camp near Villa Romana, another dramatic classical place, but the nearby campsite proves not to be open. Though the sad young woman with baby at hip (as vaguely, as evasively left in charge as the Balkan stand-in at Agrigento's campsite) seems unwillingly-willing to let them stay here anyway … it's a depressing, overgrown old house with a stagnant pond, and a wired-off enclosure of which they would be sole tenants. Upon consideration, they'll keep moving.

Freya's headset, tight on her head, is ticking its techno.

In counterpoint he starts singing: *You wanna be in my gang my gang my gang you wanna be in my gang, Wo Ye-e-ah.*

"Sorry?" she says, pulling out an ear-piece.

"Nothing, sorry, love".

… *you wanna be in my gang, Wo Ye-e-ah.* A manifesto not strong on detail, whether from Gary Glitter or Benito Mussolini or Adolf Hitler. But to the jobless yob or resentful little guy, it may seem to offer the only way up into the place where he can feel the way he wants to feel. Even today they might very well look toward *Il Duce*, up there offering them his rugged profile and shoulder-padded uniform, speech so supremely hubristic – sound, rhythm, rhetorical repetition; pause, profile, pause – for a moment perhaps they can believe: We should be, we can be, we *deserve* to be powerful. By association, by imitation, by following. Big boys grouped in a bunch round a Leader. The drug of the rousing, intimidating half-time team-talk.

Yes, yes, and it's all still there even in the circus of the Premier League, he says later to Freya. (It's lunchtime. She's munching her ham-and-cheese ciabatta.) Look at the arrogant Supermanager. Look at the big centre-forward run to the touch-line wall after the goal and beat his chest. Look at the little guy's euphoria at his part in the tribal dance with the scarf. Look at the great tattooed lug on the Sunday morning's park pitch, barely capable of a broken trot, yet every gesture an absurd mirroring of his Saturday hero – this fantasy justifies his brutality too, his spitting threats at the opposition, his occasional bad-boy glory of the red card. The rules of the game may give the ref some legal say on the open field, but just you wait until me and the boys find you in the car-park afterwards.

Hmm … Yeah, see what you mean Dad. She goes back to her book.

All the roads, in this back-of-beyond Sicilia, offer stretches which, like Greek tragic actors, stand on little stilts. And even on the best of these SP and SS ways, you can find three-inch-wide, six-inch-deep cracks across the full width of the carriageway. Signs in the hills read: *Bandi rumorosi*, which he naturally associates with the necessary tarred repairs, and the metal expansion-joints spanning between prefabricated concrete plates of carriageway every hundred metres or so. In fact, these signs refer to worn-away rumble-strips on the edge of the road, intended to make a racket to tell you if you're starting to fall asleep at the wheel.

No chance right now, in his case; though could it be that the navigator's dozing a little?

These roads reduce to a single carriageway for significant stretches; and next, in fact, even the rumble-strips are nibbled off in places by subsidence, erosion or heavy vehicles edging past each other. A wheel over one of these little bites off the side of the road could possibly tip you off on your side in the rough scrub – but in the worst spots, they might send you rolling over a drop. On this route they seem always to be on his right, these drops – that is, of course, the passenger's side. No wonder her eyes are closed. When the Muse is with him in such spots (for instance, recently in Morocco) *she*'ll tell him, in no uncertain terms, it's too dangerous, and out of consideration for her understandable fears he'll find an alternative route if there is one. Now, in her absence, he wonders if he's brought Daughter No3 on a mission whose dangers a better father would have researched more exhaustively in advance.

Freya's eyes, open again, are back on the map. He, tiring in his turn, screws his courage to the sticking-place, and his eyes to the minutiae of the road surface, and flinches at every jolt, curses silently every single rock or piece of detritus, every black hole he glimpses ahead. Lotte, marvellous Lotte, rolls and whines, bangs and jolts onward, unconcerned, apparently unstoppable.

Like so much else in his life, he reflects, Lotte stands for more than she actually is. Therefore what she is must be even more carefully taken into account, and guarded. She's eighteen years old now, give or take. Only a little younger than the young navigator. But van-life, like dog-life, isn't to be calculated in human years. He doesn't dare think right now, let alone say aloud, that Lotte has never had a puncture, in the five years he's driven her, and on some terrible roads – but never, he reflects, roads as continuously raddled as these. In fact her only serious mechanical "moment" had been three years before, a mere twenty miles out from home, on a very short trip over to Manchester. Cylinder-head-gasket. See, there it was, out of a clear sky ...

Chapter 30

Game of Roles – infection of inflection – Enna, Gerbini … – quiet – Nicolosi

"The Rules Of The Game" is the English translation of the title of a 1918 play by Pirandello (the well-known Sicilian fascist): *"Il Gioco delle Parti"*.

Literally it means, "The Game of Roles". It's a play the Captain has reason to know well. Out of a clear sky, you might say, at the end of Act One, an egg, thrown accidentally-on-purpose out of a window by a wilful young woman, strikes a passing aristocrat (sort of a "silly mishap", Cyril) and sets in motion a fateful chain of events which will end in a death. On one level, this plot-line mocks the beginning of World War I.

In 1970 the student-Captain – same age then, as Freya in his van today, acted the role of Guido Venazzi in a performance of Rules Of The Game, Act I – to win, as part of the small College cast, first prize in the Oxford University freshers' drama competition. A keen literature and drama student, who'd already read *"Six Characters In Search Of An Author"*, and acted in Brecht's *"The Caucasian Chalk Circle"*, *and* Halliwell's *"Little Malcolm and his Struggle against the Eunuchs"* in Sixth Form, he had naively believed he was well-up-on the basics of modernist 20th Century drama: masks, alienation, dramas created in frames-within-frames.

Anyway, on auditioning for *"The Rules"*, he was shoe-horned into the part of Guido by a driven young director who became furiously-determined to remove any traces of his northern accent. Admittedly, they both thought at the outset that this would be easier for him than it was to prove; he'd always thought himself a good mimic. In any case, that first Term had been nine weeks' total immersion in the Oxford environment, shoulder-by-jowl with smart-arsed public-schoolboys at every lecture, tutorial and be-gowned College-Hall mealtime. So it might be thought he'd find the accent easy to absorb. But rehearsals would prove an exhausting experience. He ended up having to go far, far … way out of his comfort-zone – and into what he thought must be absurd, grimacing *caricature*! … until, dangerously, at the last moment, the director[1] finally and grudgingly accepted his impersonation as "right". It was, extremely, right. They won the prize. For which, he had by this time been forced, physically, intensively, literally, into completely alien stance, vocalisation and gesture – to act and speak, in every phrase, convincingly the aristocrat.

The final performance took place on the Friday night of the final week of his first university term – after which, he remembers, there was a terrible, endless, screaming party, he didn't sleep for 36 hours; and for the first time in his life thought he might go mad, his mind racing; brain and body completely, it seemed, dislocated, hallucinating.

On return to his Yorkshire home, only a few days later, he would be walking his Sixth Form girlfriend Kath to the cinema. Suddenly she whirled around, yanking him roughly by a sleeve, to splutter through her tears "A' you tekkin the PISS?" Thus would he discover: his own real voice and actions had been infected, quite possibly permanently, under the previous Term's "direction". Or dictation …

Pirandello, he thinks. Character and role; reality and performance; intellect and passion; sanity and madness. All these distorting mirrors, reflecting unreliability, instability. Roles …

Roles. At times, he even thinks of himself as the Captain. Where is he? On the road. The road where? The road away from Kaos.

Where are we now?

Just past Enna, says Freya, pulling out the earpiece. I think we need to turn off at Gerbini.

---

[1]   – who now writes for the Spectator –

On then, through the hot afternoon they roll. They wind, rattle and plunge through a curious, hilly, scarcely-populated landscape: yellow roads on the map, grey dusty roads through green dusty hills. Mount Etna is now excitingly placed before them: impressive, to say the least. There's a gleam of white on its tip. Turning left at Gerbini (another set of landing fields Cy's squadron bombed during Operation Husky, then took over and flew out of) they'll have travelled almost the length of Sicily in a day.

And no, those are not airfields any more. Catania's busy international airport is closer to the city, though back then *that* was the German airfield, from which the Malta convoys had been mercilessly attacked by Junkers 88s – and which Eric Newby and his companions had been sent to sabotage in August 1942, only to be captured.

Gerbini, he thinks … Dad flew a lot of missions from there, including the hairy one on the Tape. And that little hill-town over there to the left – is Centuripe, population 5,000. They bombed that in their last sortie from Malta, before the army eventually took it. And now, oh God, suddenly there's hardly a road-sign around here that points to somewhere 223 Squadron *didn't* unload bombs on …

Centuripe, Troina, Adrano, Paterno, Randazzo. Cy had *never* pronounced *those* names with relish …

Where are we?

Gerbini. Turn left here. See, where it says Paterno?

You're quiet, he says.

So are you.

Yes, he says, OK. Did I ever tell you – But the wires are back in her ears.

Why wouldn't she be indifferent to everything but her music, her book, the map and above all, the daily destination, the sense of movement – motion that should ultimately take them to somewhere he imagines she may accept is really Somewhere, out of these obscure back-roads? To a rendezvous with her sisters, in a proper hotel, with a present-day reason for going there and being there, an Event, and people in beautiful clothes … In the meantime, she'll certainly be OK; it's travel, without real action required. Like himself, as a post-graduate student in the 1970s – travelling by train at ten miles per hour through Yugoslavia, when that was still one long, seemingly-medieval, agricultural country – she too, is proving capable of patient inaction for as long as may be required.

And bang ahead of them is Mount Etna herself ... The guide books tell the Navigator they need to use the town of Nicolosi as a base camp; the Caravan Club Book tells her how to find the campsite; and so she does it, beautifully, by the Book.

The climb to Nicolosi is long, winding and at first, quite built-up ... Curiously, as they climb, the peak and its hidden crater seem to draw back, upward, darkening.

Chapter 31

Sightseeing airmen – Catanzaro, flak-dodging – the spin, and the tape starts spinning – site and communities – caravanning, fifty years on – a fly on a volcano

The 223 Squadron Record tells the Captain that his father, too, might once have been on the ground here in Nicolosi – on 27th August, 1943:

> The … day was a stand-down period, and parties of airmen visited Catania by truck [from Gerbini], and on to the end of the road up Mount Etna via Nicolosi. Mount Etna at the time was quiescent, dominating the airfield close by, with thin wispery [*sic*] plumes of smoke from the top …

But the *morning*, at least, wasn't a "stand-down period" for Bob Connell's crew, in their favourite machine, Baltimore IIIa, 342 P "Peter". 223 Squadron had started its work, against mainland Italy from Gela, their first airfield on Sicily, in mid-August with the strike on Palmi. Now, from the Gerbini airfields, just south of Etna, formations which included "P "Peter", attacked Catanzaro, in Calabria, three times in five days. Cyril's log for the day reads:

> 27.8.43   0920   Ops40 as briefed. Catanzaro.   24   B25s, 12 of us, 24 of 3W.SAAF.
>
> Escort 60 Warhawks. Met by 1 Spitfire wing on way home. 4 x 500lb. No E/A. Good deal of A/A all the way from target till out to sea off Pizzo. 2hrs 40.

An ancient city with many ancient connections to Greece and Asia Minor, Catanzaro was traditionally a thriving centre for silk and the production of velvet. It boasted a fine cathedral, a beautiful marina. Unfortunately for its 90,000 inhabitants, by 1943 it was also a centre for Calabria's regional railways and for connections north by road. It had been bombed numerous times by Allied formations of medium and heavy bombers as soon as they had airfields within range, from February onwards. The cathedral, and swathes of of the town's streets, had already been destroyed. Then in August, Desert Air Force/NATAF started to concentrate its "light bomber" forces on the town. Those patched-up railways were smashed up once again, the marshalling yards at Catanzaro Lido in particular.

One curious fact: since these raids, Saint Antony of Padua has been revered in the town. Why? The entire rail depot and marshalling-yard, in a few minutes, had been transmogrified into twisted rails writhing up around an acre of shattered sheds. Yet as the dazed railwaymen tottered back out together from their bolt-holes, to survey the devastation … they discovered not only that all of them had miraculously survived… but that in telling contrast in the midst of the wreckage a single, pious statue of Sant' Antonio (previously not a popular feature among the largely-communist workforce) still now remained vertical – the only upright structure left in the landscape. The Saint's holy influence had saved not only his likeness, but their lives too!

In Italy, nobody argues with a miracle. There's still a festival in town at the railway station every year to celebrate this one.[1] However, it isn't known exactly how many inhabitants of the town had been killed in the many other air-attacks, before Allied troops finally occupied it on September 10th, and then moved on.

Perhaps, for pleasure in the afternoon, they went and did their sightseeing of Etna. But just eight days after this Cyril would encounter the great volcano, around which Bob's crew flew fourteen sorties, from a more dramatic angle:

2.9.43   1620   Ops as briefed 44. Gun positions. 12 of 55Sq., 12 of 223. Escort 4 Spitfires ea sqdrn. 6 x 250lbs. Only 9 of 223 reached target. Second box broke up in thick cloud. S/board motor cut and a/c[2] went into a spin. Unable to rejoin formation and returned to base. Two others returned without bombing also.

This event became the origin of "the tape"…. of 1982. Twenty-eight years ago. Recorded thirty-nine years on from that flight.

---

[1]   For this account, I'm entirely indebted to the marvellous Tim Parks: *Italian Ways* 2013 Harvill Secker

[2]   a/c = aircraft

It sounds now, as if the words he recorded, Cyril had written down to read into the little mike. If so, he must barely have been well-enough sighted, by then, to read them. Or maybe the Old Man chewed it over in his head, until he had it all rehearsed. The recording's interrupted, in any case, with the bangs, hiccups and bumps which were the inevitable accompaniment to stop-start recording on a little portable cassette player of the time:

"*September 1943, Over Mount Etna.*

"*In the Second World War, my military profession was that of Air Gunner (and I'm drawing my old age pension next week, and I'm still here, so That's All Right).*

"*I don't know whether it affected many other fellows the same way, but it did strike me that, if I were to be killed at this time, I hoped it would be by enemy action. The longer the War lasted, the more this feeling hung over me that I should be very annoyed, indeed, if I got killed in some – stupid mishap or other – and St Peter would probably giggle when I reported in at the main gate, and might even pull my leg a little…*

"*Well, on September 2ⁿᵈ, 1943 there occurred one of these silly incidents which I've just been talking about – the sort of incident, in which one could easily get killed feeling very foolish and very cross.*

"*I was a member of a light-bomber squadron which had come up the desert supporting the Eighth Army. We flew in formation in daylight, and our main purpose was to support the army in the field. We were stationed at this time at a place called Gerbini, on the Catania Plain in Sicily, and we set off, about mid-afternoon this day, to attack a target somewhere in the toe of Italy. This was the day before the invasion of Italy commenced.*[3]

"*We were a force of twenty-four aircraft, made up of four formations of six. My own aircraft was number four in the first box of six, and this meant, effectively, that we were the leader of the second three in that six.*

"*It was a nice, fine day and we were just about crossing the coast of Sicily when the ridiculous thing happened. The leading pilot, intent no doubt*

---

[3]   He means, of course, of the Italian mainland

*on his instruments, was nevertheless not looking where he was going, and
his instrument course took us slap into a very big cumulus cloud. I, in my
turret doing my routine sky-search, turned my turret just in time to see
our entire six disappear completely into this huge cotton-wool ball.*

*I have no doubt that what happened next was that we did a most
spectacular 'star-burst'[4], finding ourselves all blind: no doubt the leading
aircraft went upwards; the four aircraft, two on either side, went outwards;
and since my pilot had, just before hitting the cloud, been looking at
Number 1's tail-wheel just a few feet above his nose, all he could do was go
backwards and down.*

*"He therefore slapped back his throttles. There was a bang, as one of the
engines cut out. And in a moment we were... on our way down..."*

* * *

Now in the gloaming, Lotte's parked away in a broad, friendly but necessarily
sloping site at the upper edge of the town. There are a few vans here, but it's still
early season, the place isn't busy and last-minute titivations are taking place.
They have quite their pick of the pitches, and Freya selects a nice one, handy
for the shower-block. She explores and is pleased the place has extensive,
decent ablutions. In that respect, San Vito was fine for her, Agrigento grim.
He's taught himself not to trouble unduly at these variations. But she should
be writing the entries for the Club's Book.

Here at Nicolosi they're closer to a local community than he's felt since
he had that curious courtship with Finale, a couple of weeks ago. There's an
enticing mountainside quality to it: and yet the site's also close to town, and
to processions of students and other young folks promenading and laughing
in the evening streets. It's In The World, this place, and at present it's getting
used to the idea that the tourists and backpackers, though sparse as yet, are
beginning to arrive to bring more World in. It feels they're always alive and
open to that, up here, but keep their own perspective.

Freya's at home, whether enjoying the youthful streets or inhabiting van-
world. Though the site's so quiet, she seems to delight in that, too – the same
way he remembers doing himself, on the Yorkshire coast near Bridlington,

---

[4]   A trained procedure for sudden loss of visibility

as a kid in the 1950s. Perhaps it's partly for the same reason: parental enjoyment. Holiday sites in summer, he's sure, operate in the same way as the visit to the Christmas panto – but in reverse. At the panto, it's a truism that if the kids enjoy themselves, the grown-ups rate the whole thing highly. Yet conversely he remembers being trained by the dramatised, experimental gaiety of his Mum and Dad, to enjoy the cheap, special week in the caravan near the gravel-pits at Reighton – and by the keenness of Ros, his big sister, for "sploring" and for finding their ways through crammed, wheeled-and-chocked, grass-paved alleyways, back to their one particular, half-creme, half-maroon caravan – weirdly-alternative temporary "home". It smelled of sweet gas, and it felt to be part of a temporary "town", a community of: other children; shirt-sleeved men flaunting braces; and mums like his own, uncharacteristically floral for that one week in a flouncy, flowered cotton dress under the indispensable apron, pegging out a tea-towel.

So now, maybe Freya has allowed herself, for one last time, to drop back into a childhood holiday of her own, re-infected with enthusiasm for a pitch, a shower-block and that sense of being somewhere new every day, out on an edge, halfway up a foreign mountain. Finding how these places work is finding out how you always adapt to foreign conditions daily, even close to home. On these slopes of Mount Etna it seems you can, at almost age twenty, still enjoy the Zen … setting out with towel and wash-bag for a short morning walk, glance up at the white peak – is that smoke, or cloud? – fit your toilette into the logistical jigsaw of others', and finally return to the bubble that encapsulates your own language, the dad and a promising smell of bacon butty.

But maybe the fact is, she also enjoys humouring him. Anyhow, she's already an old hand at these larks – holiday cottages when little, then camper-vanning with dad and tenting with mum.

He's pleased with how she's picked up some of his travelling style too, head in a book. Then again this mirrors back to him his own self-absorption, dreaminess, reticence. Was that entirely a helpful legacy to pass on?

Underneath it all, he feels, when he stops distracting himself, pretty dreadful. This'll be his third consecutive day of hearing nothing in answer from the Muse. He feels, illogically, that after the events she's had to put up with in the last couple of weeks, *anything* could have happened; and, as now he hears nothing, that must mean that it has; and that his punishment for absence is – not to be told.

It's almost as though – in his head – it's she, not he, who has placed herself on a far tip of Europe, a fly clinging to the side of a volcano.

After that rattling drive yesterday, they won't go far today. After thoroughly imbibing the site, in the late afternoon they toddle back down the curving main road to find food. Finding somewhere open so early is a bit of a challenge, but eventually they find a rather Swiss-looking *trattoria* with German beer – where they can eat pizza. Expensive, but a result.

Then, tentatively, they take Lotte on an exploratory expedition, up the mountain. Above Nicolosi the road, well-paved and of a comfortable width, begins a process of uphill meanders such as are familiar to any driver among mountains. It reminds him a little of the Puy de Dome (4,800 feet, i.e. roughly one x Ben Nevis). It also recalls another climb, up from the French border and on, higher, on a minor road into the Spanish Pyrenees. He was with the Muse that day, and the winding climb (to nearly 8,000 feet) had been a horror for her: the precipitous drop of scree was on the right, the passenger-side, all the way up …

You won't get much change out of 12,000 feet, up Etna.

They park at a big lay-by, having got a taste. He photographs Freya, she him, and they agree: yup, they're still up for the assault on the summit. Tomorrow's the day.

Chapter 32

Etna

Next day, they start early, telling the van-site host where they're headed.

He smiles slowly. I'll see you later, he says. Go easy.

"In the turret, I had a grandstand view, of a tail-unit, and a wing on either side, rotating around me, as the aircraft went very nearly vertically downwards. The inside view of a spin – is not encouraging. I dropped out of the turret, onto the floor of the aeroplane. When I got there I realised that my new viewpoint was hardly more encouraging. I could see, through the transparent bottom hatch, that the spin, as we went down, was showing me 180 degrees of sea and rocks – and 180 degrees of what I recognised as the crater of Mount Etna, with a lazy wisp of smoke spiralling upwards.

"How long would it take?"

Below Lotte's windows, the plain is already hazy, viewed eastward, then westward, on successive corners of the winding road. And already it seems very far below. It is. The town of Nicolosi itself has 2,300 feet of altitude. The lower cable-car station will be at 6,300 feet. The Captain learns only later that diesel engines operate less efficiently, the higher you go. Fortunately, Lotte doesn't know this either; in any case he doesn't push her. The gradient never feels excessive, but a steady climb of four thousand feet is to be treated with some respect.

Each time they look, the vistas below them, beyond the double-bends, become vaguer, extending to still wider horizons cloaked in thickened atmosphere. And now they're peering to grab these glimpses, round great brown-black boulders: old lava of how many previous eruptions?

Freya's loving it. She isn't reading now, her earphones are out of sight, her face is lit. She's delighted as much as he is about where they're taking themselves. Lotte remains impassively Teutonic, work-woman-like, second and third gears shifting automatically.

Etna, too, has her own working rhythm. Lately this has been accelerating. So excited are the Captain and his daughter by the project, they've failed to notice the historical trend, simply because they haven't read it up. This is a very active volcano, as volcanoes go. In fact, though they don't know it, in ten years since 2000 Etna has produced six major eruptions – four from her flanks and two from her summit ... She's been quiescent since 2008 ... That's two years ...

No doubt Freya believes he's got it sussed. He hasn't, but he reckons quietly that if there's a problem, well, these days the seismologists will know about it, and shut the mountain down. Lotte keeps climbing. Now the landscape is entirely dominated by huge black turds of lava, black earth. These lumps, or rather dumps, are formless, reflect no light. They are in themselves somehow threatening.

'*Major 20th-century eruptions occurred in 1949, 1971, 1981, 1983 and 1991–1993 ....*'[1]

It takes half an hour to reach the base of the cable car at Rifugio Sapienza. Only a couple of impatient cars have overtaken them on the way up. The cable-car base comprises a very large car-park, in front of a long wooden structure (toilets, tickets, cafe, shop) – which as it turns out, replaced one destroyed by lava in the eruption of 2002-3.

'*Since 2000, Etna has had four flank eruptions – in 2001, 2002–2003, 2004–2005, and 2008-2009. Summit eruptions occurred in 2006, 2007–2008*'.

In anticipation of a lengthy sojourn on the summit, they make use of the ablutions here, pack up their small rucksack-lunch-and-drink, and board the

---

[1]   Source: wikipedia (*passim*)

cable-car. A young French couple hop in to share their cabin and, swaying gently and chatting politely, looking about them at unfeasible volumes of space, they ascend another 2,000 feet and climb out, now at 8,200 feet – onto snow.

> '*The most recent collapse event at the summit of Etna is thought to have occurred about 2,000 years ago, forming what is known as the Piano Caldera. This caldera has been almost-entirely filled by subsequent lava eruptions, but is still visible as a distinct break in the slope of the mountain near the base of the present-day summit cone …*
>
> '*An eruption on the morning of 13 May 2008, immediately to the east of Etna's summit craters, was accompanied by a swarm of more than 200 earthquakes and significant ground deformation in the summit area. The eruption continued at a slowly diminishing rate for 417 days, until 6 July 2009, making this the longest flank eruption of Etna since the 1991–1993 eruption that lasted 473 days. Previous eruptions, in 2001, 2002–2003, and 2004–2005 had lasted 3 weeks, 3 months, and 6 months, respectively.*

At the top station, the view down the route of the cables is extraordinary.

And again, the summit's not visible …It's early May, and they've climbed out onto grey ash, compacted into patches of melting snow. They're surrounded by buses that remind him of those elephants on stilts from Dali: minibus-bodied, perched up high, on huge-tyred wheels. Beyond these, all they can see are piles, banks and sliced canyons of snow, smudged as if with artists' charcoal. Logic says that after regular renewals of snow, a light dusting of ash must constantly gather on its surface, from the air …

Freya near the top station, May 2010

They could pay for a place on a bus, but Freya's absolutely with him on this, too: they can walk to the summit from here. "Forty minutes or so", they were told yesterday, and that it would be cold. It is. At least they're properly-dressed, and set off briskly – but not as briskly as the French couple, long-striding, who are soon a hundred yards ahead.

As this older man and his youthful daughter reach that hundred yards themselves, at last a view, up and across to the summit, opens up for them. The air is crystalline.

It is, he decides, like walking on a gigantic orca's arched back, towards its dorsal fin.

On they trudge. After half an hour it's clear they still have a way to go. Moreover it occurs to him that she's been carrying the little rucksack, out of which they've been sipping periodically from bottles of water. "My turn," he says, with customary gallantry.

"You sure?"

"Yep. No probs."

Quizzically, she hands him it. Five minutes later, she's well ahead, striding easily. She's eager to summit, bored with his slow trudge and that's fair enough but – how come this little backpack is so heavy?

Now she's turned round to await him near the top of the track. They're surrounded by more huge black-and-white shapes. The "forty-minute walk" has taken him an hour. A richly-dark blue noon sky has settled round their heads, gripping their skulls with ice-fingers. They sit together on a bench with their backs to a black hut, next to a dumpy Swiss woman who is complaining in a selection of languages to anyone and no-one: "It is too cold. It is too far." But nothing is too cold or too far to a man and his daughter who have made this agreed height, and are eating the sandwiches they made and packed with such anticipation, so long ago, so far down, in that other, normal world that was not the arched back of a killer-whale.

This hut against which they now sit (he and the woman, as Freya strolls off to explore) marks the *Rifugio del Filosofo*. It isn't a philosophical refuge now. It sells hot coffee and a few postcards. Unusually, the Captain makes no effort to wax philosophical either. More practically, it's occurring to him that before this ill-researched ascent, he never bothered to question whether an altitude of ten thousand or more feet might affect *his* physical performance, let alone Lotte's. He's very weary at present and rather light-headed. These sandwiches are absolutely the best he's ever eaten, and this is the best place he's ever been.

So he laughs, when he sees the high, diamond-cutting vapour-trail of a jet-liner climbing a good forty thousand feet above this, the tallest volcano in Europe.

"How long would it take?

"A regular, metronomic, alternate view of wet rocks and smoky crater was rather unnerving, to say the least. It seemed to not get very much bigger each time round. Perhaps there was a bit of time yet...."

Is there a bunch of folks right up there in a 747 looking down into this crater? Too high. Too high to bother. He suppresses something like a giggle, wolfs another ciabatta and tries to apply an even longer view.

The original Filosofo of this mountain, Empedocles the Grecian, was born in Agrigento (then called Akragas) and lived, 'tis said, roughly between 490 and 430 B.C. Although for most people now that feels like a time of myth and legend as much as of verifiable history, and although very little of his original work survives, we do know from later sources that he had a serious reputation among the pre-Socratic Greek sages.

And there's that story about him which some including Matthew Arnold took seriously: that Empedocles ended his philosophical life by throwing himself into the smoking maw of this very volcano – as proof, the Captain supposes, of his belief in soon-to-be-achieved reincarnation, and/or perhaps to presage the ascent of his soul to the region of the blessed. There should surely be limits though, even for the most inspired, in search of the ultimate rhetorical climax?

Some versions of the story tell that the mountain then threw back one of his sandals! That could have been a bit of derisive spitting on the part of Aetna the fire-goddess, at the presumption of any mortal to an immortal soul – ptui! Or perhaps, it was a good proof of Empedocles' prophesy – if all that was cast back was a scrap of his material trappings. What need has an immortal soul of mortal soles?

Then again, the whale threw back Jonah, complete and repentant. But that's another story entirely, isn't it? Isn't it?

"In the turret, I had a grandstand view, of a tail-unit, and a wing on either side, rotating around me, as the aircraft went very nearly vertically downwards. The inside view of a spin – is not encouraging. I dropped out of the turret, onto the floor of the aeroplane. When I got there I realised that my new viewpoint was hardly more encouraging. I could see, through the transparent bottom hatch, that the spin, as we went down, was showing me 180 degrees of sea and rocks – and 180 degrees of what I recognised as the crater of Mount Etna, with a lazy wisp of smoke spiralling upwards."

Aaargh. But if *you* were to plummet from the heavens, as ingloriously as Bob, Jack, Cliff and Cyril that day, and even as the result of "some stupid mishap or other", you would need to be desperately unlucky, or to aim your light bomber very accurately, to land exactly in Etna's crater. Although she does have several vents, both at summit and flank, their openings are narrow, obscure, crooked.

The Captain and Freya both peer into and photograph quite closely one of these grinning, smoking, sulphurous vents.

What needs to be said, thinks the Captain as they turn to walk (yes – proudly, delightedly – again, *not* ride) back down to the top of the cables – what needs to be learned in fact – is that we can all behave on top of an active volcano in the same way as we do everywhere else. It's a circumstance best coped with by pretending that the top of an active volcano is *not really where we are*. Yes, yes, we've travelled across a continent to be here. Yes, yes, at least you, Captain, can say that you had a particular personal reason to rendezvous with this particular mountain, rather than that it just features on your (gag, gag) "Bucket List". And yes, though not quite like Croagh Patrick pilgrims on their knees, at least both of you chose to experience it as physically as you could. Well you did walk the *last* bit. You toured that rim, yes, yes, and photographed … sky … ash … snow …

A line of other folk on a rim. Silhouetted. Like Bergman's Dance of Death. Smoke.

But were you *actually* on top of an 11,000-plus foot volcano? Did you *feel* as you stood there that this place on which you walked was a permanent battle-field between earth, water, air and fire, always in flux, never safe?

Well, yes … actually.

And did you cope with that "experience" somewhat by eating sandwiches and taking pictures and congratulating yourself that since so many other people were also here, you were obviously safe and this place was normal – not the highest and most unstable bit of the planet you've ever stood on?

Captain?

Captain? Yes, OK, you do look really cool in those sunglasses and that hat. Yes, very cool. Quite the traveller.

Down?

Yes, let's go down now.

Freya? So – how was that?

Cool, Dad. Really cool. Thank you so much for that.

Earth, air, water, fire. The identification of those four "elements", the fruit of Empedocles' insight which held sway across Western European thought for two thousand years, all the way into the Middle Ages and even beyond: Where better to think of them than here?

Yes, even water, melting from ice like tears, because of the fire in the earth – and in the air, too, from the other great fire spearing down out of the heavens. Pure blue air, and blue pure Nothing above it, except for the sun-fire. Black earth underfoot thank goodness – yes, earth. Yes and even fire below it too, and so near to this blackened surface, your feet can feel it through your shoes. They really do. Around you – all this, all this – air: but rarified, so as to make you gasp a little; more-than-normally transparent, too, to let you see so far; and to let you see how much further you can't see.

A glimpse in a lens. This slim, neat young woman. His daughter. On a brink. A flick of smoke and an ocean of aerial distance, behind her. Her head to one side smiling, maybe humouring … Cold, making you blink. A little water, produced from the eye, again, there.

Jump in!
– ha! ha! the cable car I mean! Look how incredibly far and small the lower station, even the car-park: tiny. Can we make out Lotte there? Work it out, shall we, where she ought to be? Yes yes, tiny tiny, top left corner. See?
Yes.
And so.
Down.
We go.

Identifying from a distance: Lotte. Home, four-wheeled; to be their home, once again, tonight.

In fact, it turns out they have a bit of difficulty getting back in. That step, below the door? The Neville Chamberlain Memorial Step? Like letting down the undercarriage of the Avro Anson? That lever? It's seized. Jammed. Stuck. It doesn't matter, they can easily pull themselves in by gripping the sides of the doorway – only a couple of feet up – but it's a matter of respect to Lotte, that he'll need to fix it pronto.

But now the WD40's nowhere to be found. Did he lend it to that lad near Hay-On-Wye?

Chapter 33

Some fortunate arrivals – and the road to Randazzo

The next day, there's just time to take stock before they move off – back down.

The Bride and the Groom have announced, by text message: that at least *they've* arrived already. In any case they had to get there early and stay in Sorrento a few days before the wedding, to make sure their registration's in proper order – and check that the venue's fully primed and up-to-scratch. Still, they all know they must all keep that other volcano in mind: the unpronounceable one in Iceland whose ash-cloud still keeps cracking like a whip in the jet-stream. Intermittently, days' worth of flights are still being postponed, and some cancelled, across all of Europe. There only were ever planned to be twelve guests at this wedding – and all from England – but they're all booked to arrive on different days, on flights from different airports. And then finally, fundamental to Laura's later visualisation of the whole project, there's the Muse's old pal Jerry the genius photographer, who's due to fly out from Liverpool to Napoli *the very day before the event*. Impossible to get anyone remotely as good, or as original, if *he* doesn't make it.

About all this, after due consideration the Captain and Freya are inclined to shrug: they have to say, *que sera, sera*. They'll be there, and now – big sister Emma – yes, fantastic! – has made it over with father-to-be Gordon, and they too'll make a proper week's Italian holiday of it. Still they can't help worrying, along with Laura. All the more reason for the Captain to know that Freya just wants to get up to Sorrento now and check that the bridesmaid dresses have arrived safely and still fit. The rest of the guest-list in all its prospective perfection and grandeur rests in the lap of the Norse gods of fire; of wind and ash in the jet-stream.

Lotte is once more set in motion on the mountain. This time down, from Nicolosi; down again to the south-west whence they came, and then a sharp right turn which will take them back round the back of Etna through green-and-black lumpy foothills ...

And oh, once again past Misterbianco, Gerbini, Paterno ... and now through Adrano, Bronte, Troina, towards Randazzo. Targets all these, for 223 and 55 Squadrons, RAF Desert Air Force, in the summer of 1943 just a month before Cyril's Etna-moment. Targets through the misfortunes of holding strategic high-ground, or crossroads, or ... through just being where the armoured traffic and infantry columns of the Axis were to be found, in this stage of their retreat.

But it feels his mind today isn't yet fully back on his Quest. Not as it should be. Maybe he's caught his daughter's urgency to be getting on to the mainland, up to Sorrento – and yet it's true also now that once again down here he really doesn't *want to look* properly.

"Centuripe Stadtansicht" by Clemensfranz – Own work.
Licensed under CC BY-SA 3.0 via Wikimedia Commons

Centuripe the other day, even glanced at in passing on that long drive to Nicolosi, has stuck in his mind (223 Squadron had bombed Centuripe from Malta on July 31st 1943). On her hill, she was no more than modest clusters of simple housing – white-walled dwellings with black sockets for windows,

like the windows of the blank, traumatised houses of Giorgio Morandi's landscapes near Bologna.

This road north around the base of Etna on the western, landward side – the SS284 – isn't a major road. Some are towns to pass through, others to pass by, off to the left – all those towns whose names Cyril *never* repeated. They're now dark (perhaps it's because of some temporarily dull, smoky weather) sub-modern, minor industrial zones. Between and through them, this road winds. There's a fair amount of traffic today, often right on his tail, another reason (maybe) that he finds it hard to stop and look? Among them there are the occasional views: green, dust-brown, hazed. To their right the volcanic slope is black with old lava-flows, lumps. It's said this has made the land here particularly fertile, good for growing citrus fruits. Yet they see little enough evidence of farming on any scale. At any rate he must keep his eyes on the road. Some of this road, really, was cut through old lava. Two-way, winding traffic ... and they must keep moving on now ...

Just need to get through Randazzo, you see ...

... just how the Allied attacking forces had felt, back in 1943. Back then, almost seventy years ago now, this road and the land around it to north, south and west were covered with the smoke and cacophony of battle.

On the 25th of July, 1943 the Grand Council of Italy finally brought about the overthrow and arrest of Mussolini. But hang on ... the new "government" of General Badoglio did not immediately surrender, and the eventual Armistice would not take place until six weeks later, after Sicily had been taken. So all the while in Sicily, German and Italian units continued to fight side by side against the invading Allies, while King Victor Emmanuel III and General Badoglio vacillated, considering surrender so obviously that the Germans had plenty of time to make their contingency plans …

Back in the shadow of Mount Etna, Randazzo was the town placed in the narrow funnel between coast and volcano through which Axis forces must retreat. Italian Supreme Commander Guzzoni and German General Hube knew that their retreat must be one of delay, delay, pull back, delay – because the major force of their army now funnelling towards the coast at Messina must not be cut off, but redeemed whole for days and months of a mainland campaign to come.

This was to be the Axis forces' own version of Britain's Dunkirk evacuation of 1940. The advancing Allies must be slowed, even if the ground had inevitably to be given to them in the end. The whole momentum of the front now made it inevitable that the German defensive line, built on Adrano and Troina and their surroundings, must sooner or later fall too.

So it was that on the 4th of August, that little hill-town of Centuripe had finally been taken by two Irish regiments at the end of a brutal contest in which, after the initial bombing, house-to house engagement had made sieves of the remains of houses.

Adrano was the next town reduced to rubble by Allied bombs; then by infantry advances – and first its taking by the Allies; then again its re-taking by the Germans; and more bombing – until it was finally taken back again, in worse ruin.

223 Squadron, flying from Malta again, had bombed both Troina and Adrano in two separate missions on the same day, July 22nd.

Of Troina, US Maj. Gen. John P. Lucas considered it the toughest battle fought by Americans since World War I. And as to the part played by the combined air forces? According to the official post-war account:

From 18 July to 6 August[1] [Allied] planes flew 265 fighter-bomber, 97 light bomber, and 12 medium bomber sorties against Troina. They inflicted such severe damage that, according to a ground force officer, *thirty-six hours were required afterwards for the engineers to make a single-line traffic passage*

---

[1]   223 and 55 Squadrons bombed on 22nd July, 0820hrs. "No opposition at all"

through the town. Yet Adrano was the harder hit. From 10 July to 7 August[2], 140 fighter-bombers, 367 light bombers, and 187 mediums battered the town, leaving it untenable.

All that, left – Randazzo, as the final possible Axis stronghold on Sicily. German and Italian troops fell back, under constant harassment and bombardment, onto that little cork of a town wedged in the bottleneck. Now, here, an important tactical and logistical decision – considering the double-edged sword of air power – needed to be made by the invading Allies.

An American assessment put it, afterwards:

'Troina and Adrano provided good examples of one of the problems which confronted the Allies in Sicily and, later, in Italy: was it wise to lay on concentrated air attacks and drive the enemy from a strongpoint when the destruction levied made impossible any chance of rapidly exploiting the situation?'

A serious question. But in this maybe *the Americans* were in no particular hurry. Thus:

'In terms of lives saved and morale strengthened, it generally seemed wise to smash the objective; certainly, a combination of strong air attack and superior firepower allowed the ground troops to maneuver and so eliminated costly frontal attacks.'

'Operation Husky' was after all a project that the Americans had seen from the beginning as essentially a British priority. Their answer therefore, in particular cases: "Save Our Boys ..."

And so – for Randazzo (population: 10,000) call in the bombers again. "Generally it seemed wise ..."

'Between 1 and 13 August a total of 425 medium bombers, 248 light bombers, and 72 fighter-bombers attacked the town; during the entire campaign 1,180 sorties were flown against it. Though maintaining resistance of the most obstinate sort, the enemy yielded to the steady pressure of the ground forces and the severe air assault, and on 13 August the Allies occupied the town.'[3]

---

[2]   223 and 55 Squadrons: also 22nd July, 1445hrs. "No e/A. Slight A/A" My italics

[3]   This extract and two above from official US war history:

"... to smash the objective" ...

Lotte's approach to Randazzo's centre is down a long, nondescript road flanked by tallish buildings with dark windows. It's hard to know if these are occupied or not. Now, here on the left, is a tatty old church, which appears to have been patched with breeze-blocks.

Now he pulls in, because he feels this can't be shirked, in the shadow of grey buildings. Maybe these few shop-fronts are shut because it's the afternoon. Maybe they never open. The two travellers jump down – (Oh, that step – needs fixing, yes –) in a place so un-picturesque he feels no tourist would ever think of pausing here. The sun's out somewhere, but it's chilly in the shade this side of the street.

He's seen photographs (as he has of Eboli) of Randazzo in 1943. A rubble-field. Worse destruction than the neighbouring fire-mountain had done in hundreds of years. Tank damage. Anti-tank damage. Artillery damage. Air-raid damage. Most of the civilians here must surely have left before, at some stage in the Allied advance – if they were able to do so at all ... He hopes so. But where was there for them to go?

Freya and the Captain now cross the road, emerging into the sun and onto a flat paved platform beside the church, giving in turn onto a leafy view of a shallow valley beyond it. A mile away, a railway viaduct. He's reminded of Isernia, bombed only three months after Randazzo, and of the failed attack on those vital bridges, and all the dead there in one day.

Suddenly to his left, he is looking much more closely at hand at a group of four sagging old men on a bench seat. He's looking at them now because they were talking, and now they've stopped. They've stopped because they're staring at him. He isn't wearing shorts – anyway obviously that's not it. They stare at him blankly. The Huesca stare. The Finale stare. Not friendly. Old men, in league. Same age as Pasetta. Children of war?

Flat caps, collarless shirts, braces. Old bagged trousers. Momentarily they look a bit like corpses: gap-toothed, sunken-eyed. Of course it's just the universal at-a-stranger stare, he reasons, but here now it drives him, the two of them, quickly back across the road again into the shade. And so round the corner they go, into sunlight again and – the Piazza. This is a wide-ish space surrounded by Sixties-style square buildings: a couple of shops; a cafe. It's a long, broad, modern space for evening promenading. Young green saplings around the edges of the rectangle. He can see at the far end, a monument. It is the strangest monument he can remember seeing ever in his life, and he approaches it with a kind of awe, of dread as if walking towards something out of focus in a sinister dream.

A peculiar, circular base. Yes, those are artillery shells acting as fence-posts all around the grassy base, to fix the heavy chains that mark it off. And that's not local volcanic stone, it's concrete.

That must be an Italian soldier up top. He's holding a grenade, but bizarrely he's wearing full collar-and-tie dress-uniform with his tin helmet.

PART FIVE – SICILIA

The inscription below his feet reads:

SI AL NOSTRO

SACRIFICIO NON

RISPONDERA LA

PACE TUTTO SARA

STATO INUTILE

The best the Captain can do with this, on the spur of the moment, is:

IF PEACE DOES NOT LIVE UP TO OUR SACRIFICE

THE WHOLE THING WILL HAVE BEEN POINTLESS

Maybe, he thinks, that should be inscribed on all war-memorials.

Below the main inscription, carved in cursive lettering, is a quotation:

L'arte come monito all' violenza

E. Arrigo[4]

(Art standing as a warning against violence)

The Captain's muttering something, almost to himself.

He becomes conscious gradually that he isn't completely alone in his contemplation. Now it is true that quite a few people are in the square, but they – living as you would expect, simply in the present time – are just crossing it to get somewhere else, or sitting in the sun around its distant edges under the fluttering saplings. Where else should they be? This monument was raised in 1977. That's a long time ago. None of his own children were even born then. And Freya, perhaps out of disinterest, perhaps because she knows this is part of what he came for, now stands well apart.

But he's not alone – to his right, and staring up with him at that strange, squat, unheroic, brutalist figure up there, stands a small girl about eight years old. Looking up, with affection? Smiling. She's wearing a brown dress with a badge. If she were English he'd call her a Brownie.

---

[4] Arrigo Boito? If so, poet and writer, and among other things Verdi's librettist. But I don't think so somehow.

He starts to wander away. He's intimidated by his own ignorance, his own inability to connect with *how* this statuary is Art warning against Violence – except that it seems almost intentionally ugly. Can it somehow be an anti-memorial? Can it be that it was erected, in their own way by that later generation, as a means of showing – horror? It seems like a monument to the hatred of war and violence. It makes no attempt to make that emotion beautiful.

He turns back towards it. The little girl has gone.

The third scroll, the one at the base, reads: (in Italian, of course)

THIS RECORDS THE PRICE PAID BY THIS COMMUNITY
FOR LIBERTY
FOR DEMOCRACY
FOR UNITY
FOR INDEPENDENCE

How did this town contribute anything, in World War 2, towards those remarkable *hopes*? Perhaps little enough, but they paid a price, all right.

And for democracy? – Alongside Hitler's Germany?

For unity? – Unity with what? Italy?

And independence, then? – Independence for what? Sicilia? That can't be it, because the two, a unified Italy and an independent Sicily, exclude each other.

It sounds like pure rhetoric, a list of praiseworthy but indistinct hopes that may have been, and may yet be, held by different people at different times. If you find yourself forced to fight, what can it be that you hope for? Why, to live. And then each in his own way, for *something* better to result than was before.

And *to whom* is this thing a Memorial? he asks himself. It seems, as much as anything, a memorial to communal Post Traumatic Shock, constructed out of excess munitions by people who felt, in their heart of hearts, My God, what is to be said, how can we say *anything*? Is it sarcasm? Satire?

Dumb, completely scattered, he drifts back to Freya.

We need some WD40, she reminds him gently. Across the main street, below the patchwork church, they find the small hardware shop. None of these Italian brands are the same as the ones in the shop his dad managed back home or the DIY shops he's used since. The goods are instantly understandable all the same, he finds, and here is the product! Hmm. *Lubrificante Aerosol* ... Eight euros! But it'll do the job. He takes it to the counter, where the proprietor kindly tells him he can get a smaller one – probably all he needs? – for less than half the price.

Just there signor. On the shelf below? Si. Grazie, signor.

What a good man. He didn't need to do that. Another Pasetta.

"And your father, *did he get back ok?"*

It was on 7th August 1943,that 223 Squadron bombed Randazzo.

However, their raid was only a small part of that bombardment, if 1500lbs of bombs per "light bomber" is actually small at all. And the full bomb-loads, often much heavier, of an estimated *1,180 more* planes hit the town over five days. The Germans were still not driven out of it. Eventually, having held it long enough for the withdrawal behind them to organise, they left in good order, at night. In good order apart from their dead and wounded. And the town naturally a pile of rubble. Generally it seemed best.

Bob and his boys had more reason in those days to be concerned for their own skins. Cyril:

'Ops37   Randazzo   2 boxes of six[5]. 6 x 250lbs[6]. Escort 6 Spits. No E/A[7]. A/A[8] over target heavy, accurate & plentiful. Turned E round Etna and were followed all the way to the coast by very considerable amount of fairly accurate flak.'

"Flak Alley", in other words. Actually there were, across various theatres of the War, a number of Flak Alleys[9], not surprisingly nominated by different airmen of different air-forces. What was it that concentrated the anti-aircraft fire just here? In this case since the whole German and Italian force was in process of withdrawing to the mainland, all its resources on the island,

---

5   Aircraft. 'Box-formation'.

6   Bombload

7   E/A = enemy aircraft

8   A/A = anti-aircraft fire, 'flak'

9   Including the Venafro valley, around Isernia, a month or so later

German anti-aircraft gun-crew, Sicily 1943

including anti-aircraft batteries, were pulled together in this one very tight area around Messina where it all was to be defended – until, with luck, evacuated. The ruins of Randazzo had been the last defence on the ground before that shore, that port, that rocky beach of potential escape.

Now father and daughter step out into the Randazzo sun and round the corner – and almost straight into the glass doors of a gleaming, mirror-countered *gelateria*. It's very close to the church, but he hadn't seen it before. Maybe it just wasn't open. Reconstituting himself as tourist, he amuses her by choosing quite a large (in memory of previous Italian trips) pistachio cone; she chooses her own multi-flavours. They step across again to the concrete platform with the view of the viaduct. Two of the old men have gone. The other two grin, with gap-toothed pleasure, now, and nod, almost giving a seated bow – to the dad and daughter with their afternoon *gelati*.

Then – back to the shade of the lowering dark street, and the van, and they free off Lotte's step with a couple of well-directed squirts from the new, small, bargain aerosol.

Check the map – turn the key and – each in their own way, put Randazzo behind them.

Chapter 34

Peaceful moments – Messina again – evacuation – lunchtime

Freya, the Captain and Lotte have hurried out of Randazzo to the coast. For their stop overnight, they find a quiet little site at San Leone. They're virtually alone here, in a field of spring flowers, and bright washing flapping its wings on a line tied to a lemon tree. Luigi the proprietor personally prepares them a beautiful pizza to share, as the only diners in a wooden 'restaurant' that feels like enough room for a sizeable youth-club. Perhaps just a little younger than the Captain, he speaks English, is kind and gentle, has little to say. Once, he says, he was a teacher too.

The next morning, it'll be onward – for the Captain and Lotte, back – to Messina, and the ferry.

And to the coast where in 1943 the Axis Army got away to the mainland – its whole remaining force – in no more than five days, between the 12th and 17th August.

The German force: almost 40,000 men, including their wounded, about 10,000 vehicles, 100 guns and 50 tanks – plus fuel, ordinance, equipment and supplies (they had already pulled out 12,000 men and their supplies before this final evacuation).

The Italians: almost 70,000 men and related kit – they had more soldiers even at this stage to pull back out of Sicily than the Germans (a fact often disregarded, because of later events – and, until wounded in an air-raid on his HQ at Enna the week or so before, the Italian General Alfredo Guzzoni had been, at least nominally, the supreme Axis commander in the defence of Sicily).

Anyway – the Axis evacuation to the mainland, according to an eminent American naval historian,

'has never received proper attention: partly for want of information, *partly because nobody on the Allied side has cared to dwell on it* ... an outstanding maritime retreat of the war, in a class with Dunkirk ...'[1]

Might we read in that a certain implied criticism of Allied tactics and strategy? We should ...

History remains very dubious not only about the original strategy of Operation Husky, the Allied invasion of Sicily (and thus partly of Italy, via football and instep) but also about its implementation by the commanders – Alexander was not-infrequently ignored by his "subordinate" generals Montgomery and Patton, both of whom were ambitious, rivalrous and headline-hungry. At one point the concerted advance north and east across Sicily had been delayed by Patton venturing off to pluck down the plum of Palermo – when he should have been supporting Monty's left. Later, Montgomery had been wrong – by about a month – when he said he'd take Catania in a couple of days' time. In practice, Monty was always a model of excessive caution in Italy; while his US counterpart in contrast played ducks and drakes even with himself, undertaking fresh waterborne landings to circumvent road-and-bridge-demolitions by the Germans along the northern coast – only to find that his landing-craft were greeted after these seaside excursions, by their own troops, who'd already got there by road anyway ...

A great deal of Allied air-superiority, we now know, had been used to destroy towns in the line of advance (Centuripe, Bronte, Adrano, Randazzo...) in a way that only added to delays brought about by enemy mine-laying and booby-trapping ...

The final result being: after all that, they let the vast majority of the opposing force escape back onto the mainland. A different "Husky" landing-zone perhaps, instead of Sicily's south coast, a spot closer to Messina – or a second landing there later – could have meant the enemy might have been cut off and effectively bottled up.

---

[1] My italics. Samuel Eliot Morison, 1962 *"History of the United States Naval Operations in World War II"* Vol. 9, Boston, Little, Brown – quoted in Mitchell and Stauffenberg, 2007 "The Battle Of Sicily", Stackpole Books

A second surrender of a great Axis army, as at Tunis only months before, might have been achieved. But instead of being strangled, cut off and captured, all the German tanks and men were rescued back – yes, and of course it was brilliantly managed – more or less entire onto the mainland, where those same Divisions, reinforced, would continue for almost the next two years to oppose the Allies again … and again … and again …

What's more absurd, and yet so easy to believe: Flak Alley – just one "For Instance…" How was it those exhausted German anti-aircraft teams were able to continue to put up so intimidating a screen of fire – Flak Alley – over their army's retreat?

Well – it was largely because they knew they could put their feet up, take a break – and sleep a perfect and peaceful siesta between 12 noon and 1430 hours every day!

How come?

Ah. Well you see they had learned that they would rarely be called into action at that time.

Oh? Why?

Because one of the great predictables of this theatre of the conflict was – the Desert Air Force's lunchtime.

Chapter 35

End of the spin

Anyway, German Lotte, grinning, boards the ferry. The Captain looks back at this rocky coastline, the limited port and huge expanse of open sky flanking Etna – and can't help but imagine the plotted order of massed military escape, sky black with flak, water covered with barges, oil, rafts, tanks, trucks, men.

And he can't help watching again in his mind's eye that German camper-convoy leave the site a few days ago at Agrigento: chart, instructions, logistics, orderly column, command, discipline.

The Tape continues:

"A regular, metronomic, alternate view of wet rocks and smoky crater was rather unnerving, to say the least. It seemed to not get very much bigger each time round. Perhaps there was a bit of time yet...

"After what seemed like a long time when all thought had departed, I realised that things sounded different. I realised that my view had changed. I realised we were going straight and level, perhaps even climbing. I got back up into the gun-turret and had a good look around. Everything seemed to be right with the world! I searched carefully round, and eventually saw at any rate part of our formation, a very, very long way away, heading no doubt towards our target....

"We went home. There was no intercom chatter, we didn't discuss the matter. We went home.

"When we had landed and taxied away to Dispersal, we all got out – and the Skipper said: "Well, they'll know, now, that you can pull a Baltimore out of a spin. I think that's new."

But can't you imagine: St Peter, standing at that Gate, saying, "You fell... down... a volcano... in an aeroplane? Go on, yer 'avin' me. Yer kiddin'."

"Wouldn't that irritate you?"

"Wouldn't that irritate you?" his dad says – his last *recorded* words, the Captain thinks, and therefore perhaps last words for posterity.

And of course, joking heavily. "Wouldn't it irritate you" if you had to explain to a (non-existent) recording angel, a Fougasse caricature in a cartoon of (not-believed-in) Afterlife, that your embarrassing semi-presence in this anecdote had been occasioned, in time of Herculean conflict, by a trite failure of the starboard motor in cloud, resulting in a pathetic falling-leaf tailspin and final screaming descent into Mount Etna's crater (or let's face it, any piece of earth near to, or far from it). A story which (or the last part only, presuming a direct hit on the sulphur-fissure) the cloud-perching bureaucrat might have wanted to pass upstairs for judgement on credibility?

So facetious, so crunchingly laboured, this final spin placed by Cyril upon an account-for-general-consumption of what was almost his *actual* final spin. It holds in a nutshell the old feller's whole philosophy and cosmology: in retrospect an incident best viewed as a poor joke, fate's facetiousness at his expense, but not, ultimately, quite expending him yet. Life, viewed dispassionately, and a War, in which one regularly had to watch one's fellows trailing black smoke towards earth, "toes pointed like a tent-peg". Life always thereafter held to be a tenuous lottery at best. Certainly, back in 1943 the best way of considering one's own ending, timely or not, was with parched economy – dry tongue across moustached, morgue-stiff upper lip. So:

"We didn't talk about it."

No, Dad, he thinks. Not until, forty years later, you were staring at a different open crater for much, much longer: a slow-motion crash of bad-news symptoms, an end no less inevitable for being un-heroic, unexceptional, all too credible. Holding the little mike, voice fading with your eyesight, the little black-and-silver Sharp poised on your knees in the armchair. Control-stick doesn't properly answer any more. Turret's sticking. Intercom's breaking up. You're flying almost blind. But at last, now, that old scare can actually cheer you! Back then, your number wasn't up yet! Someone's hand (Bob's – but hadn't he really helped to get you into this in the first place?) had grabbed your collar and set you back up on the swing! And he could even claim he'd done something useful, while scaring you witless. "At least they'll know now that you can pull a Baltimore out of a spin."

Well the Captain is pleased that you could pull a Baltimore out of a spin. This is after all one clear circumstance to which he owes his own, and his brothers' and sister's, earthly existence.

If it actually *was* news that the plane could be righted – it speaks again, to how little the machinery of war was tested before being handed over to aircrew in action. Or maybe it says more about the skipper's ability to bluff his way out of a bad blunder ...

As it happens Joseph Heller, celebrated 1960s author of "Catch-22", in his 1998 memoir "Now and Then"[1] gives his own recollection of a remarkably similar experience in the skies over Italy. Heller's plane, a B-25 Mitchell, was a size larger than 223 Squadron's Baltimores, with a larger payload and in the American style, more defensive armament. And while the Captain's dad was the gunner on his plane in a dorsal turret, Heller was the bombardier on his, in the nose compartment, looking forward and down. Heller's account:

> "... then our whole formation of six planes wrenched away upward at
> full throttle into a steep and twisting climb. And then the bottom of the
> plane just seemed to drop out: we were falling, and I found myself pinned
> helplessly to the top of the bombardier's compartment, with my flak helmet
> squeezed against the ceiling. What I did not know (it was reconstructed for
> me later) was that one of the two men at the controls, the co-pilot, gripped
> by the sudden fear that our plane was about to stall, seized the controls
> to push them forward and plunged us into a sharp descent, a dive, that
> brought us back down to the level of the flak.

---

[1]   Joseph Heller: 1998 "Now and Then: A Memoir – from Coney Island to here" Simon & Schuster

"I had no power to move, not even a finger. And I believed with all my heart and quaking soul that my life was ending and that we were going down, like the plane I had witnessed plummeting only a few minutes before. I had no time for anything but terror."

If there are striking similarities between this extract from Heller's memoir (his incident arguably the more terrifying, since it took place under direct enemy fire) and his dad's tape, well – the common factor is simply the panic induced by a crazily-unheroic event: "some sort of stupid mishap". The contrast lies only in the two treatments. In his, Cyril tries a light exercise in facetious understatement. But ten years further on, in the 1990s, his modernist scalpel un-blunted still, Heller directly presents what these moments really were, for both of them: absolute, blind terror.

And how was the end of the American novelist's spin?

"And then just as suddenly – I think I would have screamed had I been able to – we levelled out and began to climb away again from the flak bursts, and now I was flattened against the floor, trying frantically to grasp something to hold onto when there was nothing. And in another few seconds we were clear and edging back ...[2]

It's hard to describe ordinary people such as Heller, back then, or his own father, from these accounts, as conventionally "brave". They were where they were because they had nowhere else to be, like hundreds of thousands of men on all sides – like for another instance Spike Milligan and his artillery crew somewhere in that Italy down below; and, like millions of ordinary Italians, lost.

Most of these airmen endured extreme fear and came out of the experience with internal scars – so much is certain to be true. They had to get back out of it and put some sort of a brave face back on. But it wasn't an elective, warrior or knight-at-arms kind of bravery. It was a matter of knowing they'd been fed into dangerous parts of a machine and by sheer luck, found themselves spat out of it all in one piece in the end. They had of course been held in the frozen grip, vulnerability, powerlessness, even as staring from their planes they rattled on to destroy tanks, communications, roads, train-lines, bridges, troops, towns, civilians.

---

[2]   The incident had already provided the opening of a memorable and horrific episode in "Catch-22"

The Captain remembers the post-War Cyril mainly for his lightness, his patience, his calm caution. In this he exemplified his world and his time. Austerity in Britain in the 'Fifties was powered by the gratitude of such men and such families to have survived a war which had been "won" only at the expense of the entire power – economic, industrial and psychological – of the country of which they were citizens. They'd almost lost the shirt off their back, but since metaphorically it had been wrapped around another's mortal wound as they had cart-wheeled to oblivion or been buried in rubble, it must be right to "count their blessings". They *had* been spat out of the machine in the end, and onto home ground. And (to mix metaphors) their glass would always be seen as at least half-full, in spite of the fact that it was mostly filled with fresh air.

And isn't fresh air good for you?

Part Six

"Come Back to Sorrento"

Look at the sea, how beautiful it is,
it inspires so many emotions,
like you feel with the people you look at,
who you make to dream while they are still awake.
Look at this garden!
Ah, the scent of these oranges,
such a fine perfume,
it goes straight into your heart,

And you say: "I am leaving, goodbye."
You go away from this heart of mine,
away from this land of love,
And you have the heart not to come back.
But do not go away,
do not give me this pain.
Come back to Surriento,
let me live!

Look at the sea of Surriento,
what a treasure it is!
Even the one who has travelled all over the world
has never seen a sea like this one.
Look at these mermaids
that stare, amazed, at you,
that love you so much.
They would like to kiss you,
And you say: "I am leaving, goodbye."
You go away from my heart,
away from the land of love,
And you have the heart not to come back.

But please do not go away,
do not give me this pain.
Come back to Surriento,
let me live!

composed 1902 Ernesto De Curtis to words by Giambattista De Curtis

– English translation

Chapter 36

A bad road, present and past – avoiding rocks – being a rock

So. That was Sicily. Once across the Strait and onto Calabria, the pair of them'll be out of the port soon enough, and he's already warned his daughter about the next stretch of motorway.

But in fact, what's worse … immediately at the roundabout on the edge of San Giovanni they are red-and-white road-block-detoured off to the left. Oh … ach, and the Autostrada is now closed, for miles north, for the next stage of those essential works. This road they're given instead snakes down all the way onto the shoreline, then on a right turn, to follow the top of the footballer's toe northwards, on the SS18.

Well, on a map it makes sense – this is the only alternative road – but it's a narrow capillary with arterial traffic fed into it, and thrombosis threatens. The SS18's what you'd call a B road. To their left there's a mere gesture of intermittent barrier between this minor road and sharp, ugly rocks sticking out of the Med just the other side of the southbound traffic; and to their right, abruptly a sheer, black cliff-face which occasionally steps right out – without looking, it feels – to narrow their carriageway even further … Mostly, there's a white line in the middle of the road. But then for a hundred yards or so, there won't be. In other words, Give Way, you'd think – except that isn't the way the locals see things. Mostly, it's car-traffic, but now and again something heavy will, and does, come bucketing south round the corner towards them …

This is the first time he's ever seen Freya thoroughly fearful on a road. Consequently so is he, and he's leaning across his wheel, judging how narrowly he's passing rock on her right and – aargh! another lorry blasting the other way on his left. They're wisecracking grimly. Later, neither will remember how long it took them to drive up the SS18 through to Scilla, but he'll never make a joke about the name of that little town again.

Then at length, thank goodness, at Bagnara they're allowed back up onto the big road. Cones, yes; signs to beware of rock-falls – fine, familiar at least – and a bit of room to avoid things, too. They'll crack on as best they can.

As they head northwards, they're quieter now. They know the job from here is just to Get There.

This dad and daughter have always been pretty quiet, but still at home in each other's company, the last ten years. They're both silent people a lot of the time, at home in their thoughts or book-words, then – suddenly, briefly, excitedly, passionately – voluble for spells of minutes together, as if all that quiet absorbing and mulling over must always broil to a surging output. Then in bursts they ignite and laugh and play each other off laughing until, once again, thoughts take over.

He'll never be able adequately to explain what contentment, peace and resolution of spirit her company, all-too-rare these days, brings him. It's true too of company with Emma and Laura, his older two – that's become a settled delight. With Freya the feeling is keener, no doubt to do with her youth and that fine, radical vulnerability of spirit. Her sisters mirror back to him – what they know he determined to give them if at all possible as children in what was often actual domestic chaos – solid, affectionate stability. A rock. From Freya though, there always flashes back this keen sensitivity as well. It aches in both of them, he reckons, in different ways: they didn't see enough of each other through her teens. Of course his whole past aches in him, difficult all the time. What *his* parents instilled in *him* (without telling) was the *requirement* upon parents to be dependable, predictable rocks. In fact, *they* seemed hardly to have any further ambition. So he regrets now, sharply, that he allowed himself to be persuaded – in the case of his youngest – that it might be acceptable to be a rock in, most of the time, a separate harbour. A fortnightly, weekend rock. As if a holiday-jaunt anchorage …

Ah well, that's done with now. It was probably "all for the best"? The point is, it's all been harder for her.

"We didn't talk about it". No, Dad.

But here she is, beside him. And they've been up Mount Etna together! They won't forget that in a hurry. He knows he never will. Her headphones are on, the map's on her knee. Sometimes she dozes, even as they bucket along what's forever a bumpy road. So right now, they're very comfortable together, indeed. He keeps tight hold of the wheel, and grins, and grins. They're flying, flying north.

Chapter 37

September 1943 – and Eboli

As Sicily was finally overrun by the Allies, on September 3rd 1943, the Italian king and government, as discreetly as they could, surrendered.

Quando Vittorio era soltanto re
Si bevea del buoncaffè.
Poi divenne Imperatore
Se ne sentì solo l'odore.
Oggiche è anche Re d'Albania
Anche l'odore l' han portato via.
E se avremo un'altra vittoria
Ci mancherà anche la cicoria.

"When Victor rose to be the King,
Good coffee was a common thing.
When an Emperor he was made,
Coffee to a smell did fade.
Since he got Albania's throne,
Coffee's very smell has flown.
We just need one more victory
And then we'll lose our chicory."[1]

---

[1]   Popular Roman rhyme, quoted Time magazine 1948

Rome had by now been bombed several times. The king and his 'government' left, for Brindisi. Apparently he no longer had any use for the crowns of Ethiopia and Albania. Mussolini, whose military fakes and fantasies had led them up these and too many other garden paths, was gaoled (or perhaps, "exiled"?) First on the island of Ponza; next on Gran Sasso, a mountain in Abruzzo, you could say between Barrea and Aquila.

But of course: German divisions, poised in the country and on its borders for just this eventuality, had already moved in to seize all the Italian hardware and defensive positions. Shortly afterwards, they would catch up with and "free" Benito again, to set him back up, as their captive puppet government, up north in Salò, by Lake Garda. Then they would build and reinforce, in sequence south to north, a series of strongly-fortified defensive fall-back Lines, and dig in to fight a tenacious rearguard action as ordered from Berlin, over every rock of the stony south, centre and eventually north of Italy. Behind each Line they would shoot suspected Italian *partisani* – though local Fascist militias were, as far as possible, left to do all that dirty work for them.

Some elements of the Italian forces meanwhile made the decision to switch to the Allies' side as they moved up from the south. But north of the Line, Fascism still "ruled", under Nazism. For Italians, on top of every other misfortune, World War II was now, as it were incidentally, their own Civil War.

A woman of the town[2] of Eboli hears garbled reports – of radio broadcasts, government announcements. She writes in her diary:

8th September 1943 –

Suddenly my soul is struck down out of the blue. Such fear!

Here we are between two enemies. One is advancing on us, claiming friendship. The others, we have had here for so long, as our friends. Now they are the enemy? What sort of politics is this? Oh, how miserably things must fall out for Italy!

A few days later, Cyril writes up his log:

---

[2] "Diario di una donna: Eboli 1943". Pub.2003 LavegliaP.Editore /Comune di Eboli. Extract: English version – present author

14.9.43   0900 Baltimore IV 561 W.O.Connell Ops as briefed 47
Close support of 5th Army. Enemy concentrations in Eboli.

12 of 55 Sq,12 of 223, escort 12 Kitties.4 x 500lbs. No air or ground
opposition.

The woman's journal continues:

14 September

*Planes pass in the pale blue sky, heavy formations overwhelming us. You
can hear distant explosions. It's a continuous noise. It's unbearable –
sometimes I just have this terrible anxiety which becomes just a desperate
wish for everything just to be over, good or bad – just be over and done.*

*It's nearly midday. Suddenly they're diving on us. We find by chance a
place in a basement in the second set of yards, already people in there,
including the priest. The door's open, the window shut, and also a skylight
high up in the wall. And here they come again, swooping, machine-
gunning, bombing, a furious cannonade. Repeated gramophone-record of
Hell.*

*A bomb explodes at a distance. And here that becomes a terrible blast
through the skylight – bits of concrete, tile, masonry. I'm choking and feel
as if at any moment I'll end up under a ruined building.*

*Then an unimaginable, violent, internal revolt. Enough. Enough. I can't
take this any more.*

*Quiet returns for a few minutes. But we know that other buildings have
collapsed like piles of twigs out there.*

*Rosetta says, "Mum, can we get out and go up onto the mountain? I can't
stand it here!"*

*"Same here," I reply. So: let's make our minds up – Dr Ciro, a friend of
ours, thinks the same. Let's decide, we say: first we'll eat something, and
then let's just go – as far as our legs can carry us.*

We bolt down some food – then, laden down with our stuff, we aim down through the old castle, as far along as the convent and then on, up into the mountainside. We stop for a moment at the refuge-hut, because once again, there are low-flying enemy planes; and then we leave; and then, frightened, we rush back in a couple of times. Then we grit our teeth and say, this is it, and we're hurrying out on the mountain. And the green trees and blue sky do put a fresh feeling of security back in my heart, and of feet on solid ground, and – if we are going to die, let's at least do it with our eyes looking up at this cobalt-blue sky. Those ruins back there, those collapsed houses with the dead lying under them, paralyse you with pitiful feelings.

We go on up, weaving between great rocks on a stony path. Then there are more trees, then a wider space with groups of oaks, then the start of a sunset, full of golden shapes …

Suddenly a powerful formation of aircraft precipitates itself on us over the mountain … Immediately we have flung ourselves to the ground behind bushes and stones. Over our heads we hear again the characteristic whistle of bombs, rattle of guns – hellish noise – and it's aimed directly over there onto the town! They pass, we get up to move on, but a few steps later they're back following us, diving towards us on the ground.

I damaged my knee on a stone but didn't feel it; my arm was somehow hurt too. I could only think of danger overhead. They bombed, strafed – our ears full of whistling din. We crawled on, to a grove of trees where we were taken by surprise by a third attack worse than all the others. When it had finished I raised my head and looked back there at my town. Nothing but huge, heavy plumes of smoke where the houses should have been.

Eboli is completely destroyed, my friend said with a sigh.

We moved on with constriction in our hearts and a great need to be as far away as possible, to neither see nor hear anything more, and so we moved always higher in the hills and up the mountain – to the Boffa family's farm at the foot of la Madonna de Carmine under San Donato.

There we enter a low, smoky kitchen full of people. They're just leaving to go even higher, because this morning bombs have fallen near the spring. Beyond the kitchen are the big stables, full to bursting with people – everywhere blankets, mattresses, sacks, anything for them to sleep on. Few words are exchanged, all appalled by the threat of death hanging over us.

Overnight a lot of the others got up and moved on again. The sky was full of so many stars, and an arc of a moon.

My group tries to make itself comfortable on the floor, on blankets where there's now some room. I sit by a table, quite close to the open door. From here I can see the mountain. I press my hands to my temples. I won't sleep. No-one will sleep tonight. Heavy planes come over again and bomb and strafe down there. Even a distant blast feels as if it's over our heads, as the building shakes every time.

Then the door's shut, and it seems that everyone's asleep. Through the window's iron bars I watch the sky glow.

One moment, I'm about to close my eyes, the next I open them with a jolt. As formation after formation passes over, I look out at a pure, dark-blue, cloudless sky, unstained – whole strips of stars are sprinkled there like crushed light. Onto that sky, there now opens one great flare. Partly it's beautiful, partly terrifying. It seems like a new sun that glows into full daylight on the mountain. All the lights of the sky are blotted out by its whiteness. After that sun, another; and another; another – a bunch of little suns have come down to spy in the night on the mountain[3], so that the point can be chosen where ruin and death can sew themselves again.

Could this be the last night of my life? Absolute anguish.

15.9.43	Baltimore IV	Ops as briefed 48	2hr 50
1430 561	W.O.Connell	Close support 5th Army. Enemy concentrations near Eboli. 12 of 223, 12 of 55. Escort 12 Kitties.	

---

[3]   Marker flares for bombing

6x 250lbs. Small amount of accurate

A/A fire. No E/A ...[4]

... In three separate sorties between the 14th and 17th of September 1943, 223 Squadron bombed Eboli and unnamed targets in its environs twice more. This was because the Allies' "Salerno landings" of a few days before were fighting their way inland off the beaches and towns in the coastal strip 10-15km to its south and west.

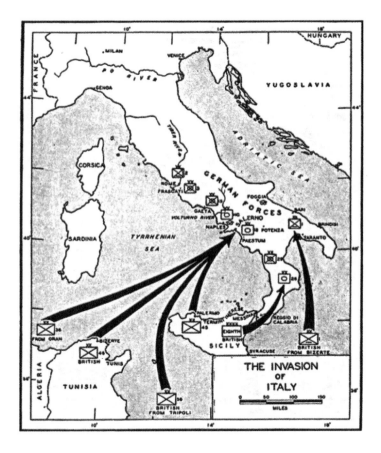

The beachhead at Paestum was a focal point in this brutal phase of the campaign, the nearby railway-village of Battipaglia was its crux.

---

[4]   The Log seems to indicate this physical "untroubledness" might have been true less than one third of the time for Cy's plane: e.g. in the Log – 'No opposition at all.'

Eboli, the point at which "Christ Stopped", had become a strategic crossroads. The Germans needed those two roads, the road north for their retreat, and the road east/west to cross the mountains with their tanks and trucks. It had become a position of considerable tactical weight. First they had brought in a Panzer Division to hold the high point, and those junctions. Now they had fully occupied the town, and brought up more artillery overlooking the coastal basin into which the US Fifth Army, under cover of their own colossal naval barrage, had just arrived.

The Allies had to bomb them out of the place. Once again,

"It generally seemed best".

Eboli, October 1943

Yes, Signora –

Now – Who were the Enemy?

Chapter 38

*Autumn-winter 1943 – Squadron moves – Foggia – mission quotas –
illnesses, mishaps*

In mainland Italy, from 1943 onwards, while the Allies had overwhelming
air-superiority, the Germans had the choice of ground, of defensive position,
of fortified line. Inevitably, the Allied air-forces used their relative freedom
of the skies to bomb and strafe those positions. In a war of attrition such as
this, even with mounting aircrew losses, it was a low-cost strategy in terms
of men and machinery.

At every step then from the south coast of Sicily to the foothills of the Alps,
the Germans dug themselves into Italian rock, dust, mud and snow, and then
moved, edged: forward, sideways, back ... Under Field Marshal Kesselring
they moved backward sure-footedly, with same careful feeling for a foothold
as expert mountaineers descending a vertical ice-face in the dark. They dug
themselves in under, round and through Italian towns, villages, mountain-
passes; they moved in their artillery-trucks, their tanks and earthmoving
machinery, over the rubble of all the above – with incredible military
efficiency, in other words with no concern whatever for the conquered,
superseded, despised Italians. Italy and the Italians were the landscape,
the ground, the cover, the no-man's-land; Italy now transmogrified into a
mountainous military topography, absorbing to the strategist, useful for
defence. For the strategic HQs, this country was no more than a 1:1 Scale
military map, a big board full of interestingly-contoured features for the war
game. Apart from military personnel there were no human beings on the
game-board. There are no civilian casualties in war games on neutral soil. In
the strategies of generals there are no individual people at all. There is only
Victory, and a History to be written by the victors.

Nor, generally, are there people to be seen even on landscapes viewed from high in the air by the navigator/bomb-aimer. There are aerial reconnaissance photos and navigational charts marked with "enemy positions", "strategic crossroads", "communications", ports and railways. These are to be imagined as empty of Italian civilians … How else are they to be imagined?

For 223 Squadron, the late summer and autumn of 1943 was particularly bad. "Malarial jaundice" – endemic in Sicily and southern Italy for centuries – haunted them now, right through to the end of their campaign. The Squadron Record from here on continually mentions it. (In North Africa, it had been "black-water fever".) The mosquitoes were biting, men started to become debilitated. It started as early as August.

Late in the month, unseasonable weather in Gela on Sicily's south coast had waterlogged the airfield before the Squadron's move to Gerbini. Rain, rain. By the end of September, Gerbini was itself unusable. Following close on the advance, they shifted to Brindisi on the mainland heel. Conditions worsened further. It was even wetter – and now colder. Winter came earlier, sharper in Italy that year. It was noted that the Desert Air Force's KD "Khaki Drill" uniform issue, appropriate for summer in North Africa, was now seriously inadequate for October in a soaking middle-Italy...

The men were heading, not just north behind the army, but towards what they hoped was the "expiration" of their operational time. How they must have longed for it.[1] There were more "stupid mishaps" – visited upon others.

---

[1]   Of course, the central issue for Heller's Yossarian in "Catch-22". In the later history:

"The number of missions required of the aircrews in Catch-22 is an accurate reflection of the reality of the war in southern Europe. In northern Europe, the crews of the 8th Air Force's B-17 and B-24 heavy strategic bombers flew deep into Germany and were often in the air for eight to ten hours at a time. Until long-range escort fighters like the P-51 "Mustang" became available late in the war, they suffered terrible losses from German fighters and antiaircraft fire. As a consequence, for most of the war the B17 and B-24 crews were required to fly only twenty-five missions before being rotated home (Freeman 29-32). In comparison, the shorter range B25s in southern Europe flew missions lasting for only a few hours, and they often flew several missions per day (Now and Then 185-6). As Heller noted in his autobiography, his quota was raised several times during his own tour. When he arrived in Corsica in early 1944, the number of missions for his group was up to fifty, and during his tour it went from fifty to fifty-five, and then to sixty. By the time he was taken off combat status, the number of required missions had reached seventy (185)." Scoggins, Michael C., 2002. Joseph Heller's Combat experiences in Catch-22. *War, Literature and the Arts.*

Cyril, as noted elsewhere, flew seventy-two missions.

Ops as briefed 55 – Montecilfone.

… Great deal of heavy cloud en route. Bombed Guglionesi in error.

Own troops.

And they were flying in aircraft which themselves were more and more battle-worn, needing constantly to be patched, rotated out, mixed and matched. Baltimore FA479, for instance, was damaged "Cat II"[2] over Catanzaro at the end of August. That was with another crew. Then on 13th October, when Bob's crew flew it – through heavy flak over Vairano – it was holed again in the starboard engine; but the plane and the boys "got back OK". Five days later, with yet another pilot and crew, over Isernia, FA479 was rendered "Cat II" again, with extensive damage to port wing and fuselage.

Bob's crew, two days later:

… Ops 60 as briefed – road junction NE of Venafro.

A/A heavy, intense and accurate. 1st box completely broken up. One shot down in flames, 3 chutes seen, 1 crashed in own lines […] all crew safe having baled out, 1 crash-landed Bari, all safe. Flew in 2nd box which returned intact. 2 holes.

The next squadron move, from Brindisi up to the newly-liberated airfield-complex at Foggia, was another horror-show. This was an area whose aerodrome, fields and roads the retreating Germans, once they were finally forced to retreat, had left mined. The airfields had already been waterlogged, but sewers had also been broken open, and quite what these ailing, tented airmen were waking up floating and then wading about in, was anyone's guess. All ranks began their stay at Foggia scouring the airstrips for shrapnel, which might otherwise shred tyres on take-off. New, sheet-metal runways eventually had to be laid. The laconic, account-book-style Squadron Record uncharacteristically starts to talk with depressed subjectivity about a "flat, dreary, featureless landscape". More to the point it begins to be noted that "in general" targets are even "more heavily defended" – and the calibre of flak shells is consistently heavier.

---

[2]   Category I = patch this aircraft up quickly

    Category II = Serious damage needing structural/mechanical repair – out of the line of active aircraft

The chance of any *individual* Flak-shell actually hitting you was always slight. But if there was a lot of it, if it was heavy and if it had your range, you were likely to be badly rattled, at the very least, and your plane probably was punctured by bits of shrapnel … And in the febrile state of worsening health and conditions at Base, more of the much-feared "stupid mishaps" began to pile up. Thus

> … on 30th October, FA 475 … was returning to base in formation from an operation, when in the region of Foggia, the turret-cupola was blown off, and the A/G Flight Sgt B------- was jammed in the turret, receiving lacerations over the left side of the frontal bone. The pilot began to lose height so as to land and free the A/G. He then felt a draught of hot air, and enquired of the rest of the crew but received no answer. He next heard a loud bang from the front of the aircraft and knew by the rush of cold air that his observer Flt Sgt F------ had baled out. His parachute opened too late due to insufficient height, and he was killed.

> It was thought that the navigator baled out on his own initiative due to the combination of the noise caused by the turret cupola, the failure of the intercom, the fire in the aircraft, and the pilot breaking formation and losing height. The pilot and WOP/A-G were uninjured.[3]

Now understandably – and it isn't unique in this respect – this is a very confused and in places self-contradictory account, even if created only for official purposes (i.e, hopefully for no-one higher-up to read). But curiously, *this* plane doesn't seem, from the maintenance records, to have ended up seriously (Cat II) damaged on that mission. The message, if any, intended to be drawn from the above account is: the CO says, if the navigator had sat tight, he would have been safe.

Baling out of a multiply-occupied warplane was *not* supposed to be a spontaneous individual decision. Then, the following day:

> '… FA 436 was hit, causing a fire in the fuselage, and left the formation. The fire was put out, and a landing was made at Capodichino, nr Naples. The Nav/B, Flt Off. R------, baled out at once after the aircraft was hit, and his parachute was seen to open, but he was later reported as missing. The other members of the crew all returned to Base next morning.'[4]

---

3   Squadron 223 record, quoted in Butterworth, op. cit.

4   Ditto

From now on there's a very strong sense (and it's unlikely that it was present *only* among those aircraft encountering first-hand damage or mechanical faults) that crews were sitting tight and tense on clouds of contagious potential panic – born of illness, exhaustion, low morale.

Though Bob's crew weren't part of either of these chaotic incidents, their mates were; and they provide yet more context for that taped remark of Cyril's that all along he had not wished to get killed by mistake. He, or someone else, could easily make a bad, panicky and irrevocable decision. He learned this from vivid personal experiences before, during and after the Etna incident, and he must always have carried the thought with him into the air.

30.10.43   Ops65 as briefed Gun area E of Carpinone …

… Good deal of very accurate H.A/A.[5]

1.11.43   Ops66 as briefed Acquafondata

… Very heavy and accurate A/A fire throughout time over enemy territory

In reminiscences recorded long after the war, Bob Connell said that they were *all* now in a fraught mental state: "You'd jump if someone tapped your shoulder". And his next sentence is, that Cyril then had a spell in hospital.[6]

Whether this was to treat nervous exhaustion, or recurring malarial jaundice, or for some other cause, Cyril must in some way have been glad of the break, from the 2nd to the 25th November, at a field hospital in Naples. And after those three weeks, even though it was back to his mates, his heart must have sunk again, to return to wretched Foggia. Ach, and their first Op (his no.67) on his return, they flew once again in… poor, patched-up FA479 again: "No opposition". Phew. (But just two weeks later, FA479 would blow up over Chieti: all four of a different crew that day, killed outright.)

 Bob Connell[7]: "I did see an aircraft one time, just alongside me in the formation – just blow up. Direct hit. And that's a bit of a frightening experience I can tell you … That's not very pleasant. Right next to you and

---

[5]   H. A/A = Heavy (meaning larger shells). So amount or number of bursts – "good deal of" – is a different category from *calibre* – "heavy/light" – for log purposes.

[6]   At this stage he had flown 66 missions.

[7]   Temora Aviation Museum: Unsung Heroes Project 403721 Robert Connell (video and audio files) Thanks again to the Connell family for this connection.

covers you in oil and … Four men dead just like that … Knew the guy, yes … We all knew one another really well, the pilots. Makes you think."

In an increasingly-neglected theatre of the war, things were falling apart.

Chapter 39

Lotte makes waves – wedding weather? – sisters reunited –
the Captain fouls up

The Captain and Freya might with more time have approached Sorrento by a leisurely scenic drive around the Amalfi coast, from south, westward a little way out to the cape, then back eastward on the northern side. But having timed their arrival so late (or so accurately) to the very day before the wedding, it's best simply to arrive. The beautiful streets are narrow, but the hotel itself's relatively easy to find. He pulls Lotte rather beautifully, with his customary reverse, into a rank of very expensive-looking cars outside the smart, flag-bedecked frontage – and they take themselves to Reception.

A tall, pale young woman in her thirties agrees that indeed yes, they do have their bookings in order. He reminds her that, by email a couple of months before, he pre-booked a parking place, so he has taken one at the front. At the front? Ah, no, that will not be possible – these are the spaces reserved for the managers, you understand, Signore.

Oh? But he has seen no other spaces.

The Guests' car park is *beneath* the hotel, Signore. She will show him. To the right of the grand glass revolving front door she takes him to view a striped barrier, a crossbar and a tunnel to the underground parking. Here he purses his lips, gesturing at the restrictive height-bar. But surely, she tells him as if speaking to child, his car will have no difficulty …

My *Camping-car*, he says.

He gestures down the line of vehicles ranked on the other side of the broad front steps. Suddenly, she sees the Hymer, and it seems she rocks a little backward on her heels.

Like a road-roughened lump of old leaden typeface, Lotte looms – too, too solid – among the gleaming *sans serifs* of the management and of, he imagines, certain wealthier patrons. Even on an overcast day their grey-silver parade flashes like a stylish mirage while, in their midst and above them, Lotte's bodywork, even if it were not coated in the dust of many roads, has obviously never in the last decade been better than a scuffed, outdated matt-cream. Her front wheels, her wryly-grinning mask and bumper protrude insolently out of line; in effect but not intention, she's become an out-stuck tongue in the face of a gleaming street. Unmistakeably a Used Vehicle, Lotte is nothing like an automobile with which this establishment, or indeed this most dreamlike of towns, should ever have had to be associated.

Ah, no, Emilia protests, trying to move confidently again upon the balls of her feet, no, it is not possible to park here!

But walking back up the steps with her and into the cool, panelled Reception, he has produced, from among all his sequenced booking-papers, an email. She has introduced herself as Emilia? So, Signorina Emilia will remember this email sequence in which, months ago, well in advance, he had explained not only the need for a parking space but had also detailed the make, the length and height of the camping-car in question, and – here – see, signorina – here is her final assurance that this would present *no problem. Signed, Emilia.*

The best Emilia can do is hold the print-out at arm's length as if trying to doubt that communications exchanged purely for convenience of internet bookings can ever morph into a physical reality so shocking.

Anyway, says the Captain quickly, we'll leave her there for now, eh?

Through he goes, into a quiet internal courtyard: where Freya, rightly sensing an opportunity for her dad to be embarrassingly-difficult with hotel management, has already joined her sisters and cousins. When he goes through, they're all sitting quietly around a couple of small tables, sun-shaded from what now seems unseasonably (and disturbingly, considering the wedding-day is tomorrow) like a fine, drizzling rain.

His three daughters, once more reunited.

They all greet him with smiles and hugs and little cries of admiration (they know he likes that) for All That Driving … Alison, cousin of the bride, and Paul, brother of the groom, have been making an Italian holiday out of their honoured-guest and best-man obligations. They look tanned, well and relaxed. Emma and Gordon look very well too, especially Emma, six months into her first pregnancy. Ian's parents, and Laura's mum and her partner, aren't around at present but they've arrived. Bride Laura and groom Ian have of course arrived in Sorrento a good four days before. Anyway all their paperwork's done now; and they've visited the venues for the ceremony and the reception – both are very much to their liking.

Oh, and... ah, and – *none* of these essential participants have been prevented in the end by the ash-cloud! They share their stories ... There were certainly some delays and bitten nails ...

Only one final significant worry now remains: Jerry, the brilliant photographer. It's a month since those Eyjafjallajokul eruptions began, and flights were just about back to normal over UK airspace ... But now, suddenly – again, following on another shift in wind-direction – nothing has been allowed to fly out of British airports for two days! The ash-cloud's well-and-truly back, and it's squatting squarely, wickedly, across the Isles like a nasty succubus.

(Unbeknown, this means that back in Leeds, while Jerry, booked on a flight this morning from Liverpool, has dutifully set off in the early hours, – it's been really without a hope. He arrives at 'John Lennon Airport' that morning to find it packed with bug-eyed would-be travellers waiting for news, any news, some having already waited there longer than twenty-four hours.)

What's more immediate, on the exotic Bay of Naples, this drabber-than-ordinary weather still needs to be fixed. That is, if the wedding-day's going to be up to *absolute* expectation. Sorrento's skies today remain grey, dampish, unimpressive, non-celebratory. This doesn't *seem* to bother Laura: "It's been dull all week to be honest. But it's a beautiful place, we've got the harpist arranged, everything's ready to go, everyone's made it!" She frowns. "And if Jerry doesn't make it, the wedding firm say they always have someone on standby. I know that won't be the same ..."

"It'll be a big day, a great day, even if the sun doesn't shine", says Emma, and calls a waitress over for more mineral water.

So here now is the rest of the World, going on heedless of one particular, imagined-heroic, solo voyage. Because all the arrivals have been in their own ways remarkable. Still in the shock of his own, now it also strikes the

Captain that he's the only *older* person here. He's in the midst of a happy, confident, ultra-competent group of young people who will always enjoy one another's company for years and decades to come … Whether he's there or not. Which is as it should be, certainly …

Freya's sipping Pepsi, across from her dad's cappuccino (with-gin-and-tonic-chaser).

Laura is saying: she and Ian are really lucky, they've got a smashing house, and they've both got good jobs, secure jobs they're good at … Ian agrees, in fact everyone agrees.

The Captain, trying to re-establish his mind back into their reality, says, "I hope in time you find you can move away from some of those cases, Laura, that kind of case-work, because I know how it can tell on people in the end". Laura's in Child Protection social work. Not easy. Not without difficult issues, potential controversy, consequent stress … She's very good at it, as he knows and her promotions prove. Even so, he knows these days that means she's only one piece of missed communication away from being pilloried on the front page of the tabloids.

"I know what you're saying, but we are still really lucky to have our jobs though, Dad." Post-Crash, she means.

"Thing is", says Freya, "Dad's never really approved of any job *any* of his daughters have taken up." She means, he's always been worried on their behalf, that something could go wrong. He's still a bit too much The Father?

He takes it the wrong way. He takes it as a put-down. Is it because, with all of them now together, and the years passing, he might be losing the limelight? He's used to taking Alison and her Paul, Emma and Gordon, Laura and Ian – couples in their own right – as an audience, still, with whom he can sit back and smile, play the Dad…. But now, whether or not he's coming back from a medieval Quest – in the midst of young working people and their futures, it's shockingly-obvious that this group are no longer themselves a Future, which needs to be guided, protected or chaperoned. They *are* this very Present day. The world, as it's been left to them by his own lot, is now theirs. They won't of course be unhappy if what they do now *incidentally* pleases him; but they know it's much better if they please – and if they do what's right for – themselves.

So, soon to start university, Freya's understandably relieved, glad now to be in the midst of this and on their level, comfortable to add her comment into the mix – But subconsciously, maybe *he's* just not ready to let go of *her* yet. And he sees her, now, suddenly and naturally, step across – from loyal sidekick, navigator to his pilot of the long road – to find her rightful place on The Other Side. What else can it be that makes him instantly so facetious, so sarky now? –

"When you ever get around to getting yourself a job of *any* sort, you'll be entitled to comment" – he says with a grin to the others. They'll all take it as Dad being Dad –

Freya's chair grates back. She sobs, and disappears into lobby darkness, around a corner, away into the depths.

"Oh Freya …" says Laura.

He staggers up to follow her, to apologise.

'You have displaced the mirth, broke the good meeting,
With most admired disorder',

he quotes madly to himself. But now he's in the bowels of an unfamiliar hotel. Trying already, again, to put something right– and he hasn't even got his stuff into his room yet!

Oh, where has she gone?

Oh. Oh. His eyes are blurry.

Probably it's Emilia that's to blame. It can't be him.

He turns around again, casting desperately about him – and here, out of blur at great speed, blocking the light from the door, beaming and bounding, irrepressibly stylish, arms outstretched full of greeting, excitement and justified self-congratulation: "Incredible! Can't believe it! I'm here!" – is Jerry the Photographer.

Chapter 40

Napoli 1944 – apologies – guests and preludes – a serious warning

Early in 1944, the Germans would desperately rustle up enough aircraft of their own to bomb Naples. Norman Lewis, then a British intelligence officer, was in Naples:

> *March 15* A bad raid last night with heavy civilian casualties, as usual [...] In Santa Lucia, home territory of the Neapolitan ballad, I saw a heart-rending scene. A number of tiny children had been dug out of the ruins of a bombed building and lay side by side in the street. Where presentable, their faces were uncovered, and in some cases brand-new dolls had been thrust into their arms to accompany them to the other world. [...] The Germans murder only the poor in these indiscriminate raids, *just as we did ...*[1]

Less than a week later, Norman Lewis again:

> *March 16, 1944*
>
> Today Vesuvius erupted. It was the most majestic and terrible sight I have ever seen, or ever expect to see. The smoke from the crater ... swelled and expanded so slowly that there was no sign of movement in the cloud which, by evening, must have risen thirty or forty thousand feet into the sky and measured many miles across.
>
> The shape of the explosion that obliterated Pompeii reminded Pliny of a pine tree ...

---

[1]   This [my italics] and other extracts in this sequence, from Norman Lewis: "Naples 44" (Collins 1978, republished Eland 2002)

What took one by surprise about Pliny's pine was that it was absolutely motionless … an utterly still, and utterly menacing shape. This pine, too, trailed uncharacteristically a little tropical liana of heavy ash, which fell earthwards here and there from its branches in imperceptible motion.

Seventy-eight American war-planes were destroyed on their landing-ground at Terzigno. Meanwhile, awestruck congregations lifted the images of Saint Sebastian and Saint Gennaro from their churches and carried them up mountain roads, to placate this horrific threat to Naples and its surrounding towns and villages. But soon the very town of San Sebastiano was being swallowed, a street at a time, by an implacable, slow-motion wall of lava.

March 22

At the time of my arrival the lava was pushing its way very quietly down the main street, and about fifty yards from the edge of this great, slowly-shifting slagheap, a crowd of several hundred people, mostly in black, knelt in prayer. Holy banners and church images were held aloft … Occasionally a grief-crazed citizen would grab one of the banners and dash towards the wall of lava, shaking it angrily as if to warn off the malignant spirits of the eruption …

The March 1944: eruption of Vesuvius[2]

---

[2]   Photo by Jack Reinhardt, B-24 tailgunner in the USAAF during World War II
Public Domain, https://en.wikipedia.org/w/index.php?curid=13705245

* * *

Back in the present moment, the Captain's found Freya and apologised.

They're both just tired – and glad to have got here so perfectly on time, they agree, and thank each other.

Still, he's very upset and angry with himself. So much so, that the news Mike is in town, has "bumped into" Laura yesterday and congratulated her, handing her a bottle of wine – she had been pre-warned but was still nonplussed – just drifts away on a breeze of relative inconsequence. Pillock.

Jerry, having stowed his baggage of camera-equipment in the twin-room he'll share with the Captain, is on an absolute high, having landed at Naples airport and navigated himself excitedly across to Sorrento. He retails the full detail of the morning's unique early-morning escape-flight from John Lennon Airport, laughs a lot, and keenly accepts the Captain's offer of a wander round the town – revelling (as who would not) in the sheer photogenicity of Sorrento. They stand and gaze across a rather misty Bay at the shape of today's quiescent Vesuvius. Then they sit in a cafe on the square and chew the fat. Jerry's suitably impressed – and as envious as anyone in the *working* world – at the pilgrimage of Lotte and her crew. At the same time, he's very solicitous about the Muse and her horrors at home. And now, perhaps he'll need to feel a bit concerned about the Captain's rather distracted state … It's possible, when she helped Laura by lining Jerry up for the gig, the Muse had foreseen that in these hours this outgoing feller might prove the very best company for her partner.

On their return to the hotel, the whole tribe's gathered. This includes the new in-laws – good people, comparatively quiet – and his Ex, mother-of-the-bride Karen, whom under normal circumstances he has studiously avoided for a long time now, with her partner Chrissie. While the Captain generally in his working life grew to be comfortable at hosting all sorts of groups of strangers and newcomers to all kinds of shindigs, none of these people here are new people, it's not a captive audience of strangers. They're close connections, acquaintances with their own expectations and perhaps like him, their own apprehensions of the coming event. Thinking of the afternoon's *faux pas* with Freya, his heart begins to sink again. He'll have to work hard now to make sure he does, and says, the right thing all the time. Thank goodness he has Jerry's bouncing bonhomie like a travel-charger to plug his own smiles and wisecracks into. But he mustn't be careless.... An active volcano stands behind him.

Fortunately, Laura's more than determined to make sure that the whole event will be well-marshalled. She also knows that leaving her father alone to front-up so significant a one-off gathering of egos, however sensitive they are to the occasion, might be a mistake. So she's sent him off to try on the quaintly-Edwardian long-jacketed suit for which he was carefully measured months ago.

If the suit fits, wear it. And it does, still. Meanwhile the bride gives everyone clear marching-orders for this evening's separate (male, female – clever girl!) dinners.

So now the Captain must get togged up in his best available casual-evening-wear. Revisiting Lotte's cupboards to fish out a smart shirt and trousers already feels like a retreat into an odd, Med-yachting dream-world. Anyway: then Ian, with his brother-and-best-man Paul, Peter their dad – and easy-going groom Gordon, the men-folk of the wedding-party, stroll off and make a very pleasant meal of it in the pre-booked restaurant. Gordon and he, the only drinkers this evening it seems, are helped to do rather well on the red wine.

The ebullient wedding-photographer wisely keeps out of all this. He's preparing for tomorrow's work, laying out his equipment and again stalking the wedding-and- wedding-breakfast-venues, preparing all his angles.

On the Captain's return, his new room-mate has just one last piece of news: "Now listen. Er ... Apologies in advance ... People – well, Kay, naturally – people say ... I sometimes snore. Quite loudly."

"I'm knackered, Jerry", says the Captain. "I doubt if I'll hear a thing".

On the twin beds, they turn in.

Chapter 41

The Day

Perhaps a railway shunting-yard? A nearby cement-mixer?

Aargh! Volcano! Vesuvius!

No.

No, just Jerry. Very, very asleep. *Still* snoring.

It's a day of magnificent, broad-cast clarity. He takes a quick breakfast, by which time the in-house erupting scrap-metal yard sound-effects have incarnated themselves into a vertical photographer who, having created his own up-to-the-minute brief, is busying up staircases and down lifts shooting a mini-documentary of fly-on-the-wall pre-wedding shots:

the groom, plus the best man and his missus, up on the roof, in beachwear on the loungers, catching these wonderful, so timely rays. Cool. Chillin';

the bride's room – transformed to efficient salon, featuring Freya, already the fully-dressed bridesmaid, all calm logistics; Emma, studious over the bride's make-up; Laura herself, t-shirted, glowing with delight, already hitting the prosecco, alternately flapping and giggling, and stressing – about where the hairdresser they promised her has got to;

the bride's father, in greater need of a hairdresser than anyone else, his thinning, newly-washed, long locks and strands all a-gley, neck and chin scrunched up over his wing collar, trousers still unbraced, checking his phone for a message ...;

the brothers now back in their rooms, deciding they'd better be getting ready, toy-fighting over cuff-links;

the bride, now in The Dress; Emma smiling, calm and still not changed up; Freya in her element; the mums popping in, out, in again; and ah, yes! She's here, the hairdresser –

bride's father fully-suited now, waistcoated, cravated, slipping into black patent shoes, and himself starting on the prosecco (steady ... bit early! ...) himself, wisecracking with the cameraman on the balcony – some market-garden-looking greenery behind him in the picture, then trees, then the Bay, then the volcano ...

the Boys now ready – or looking ready – to go – a bit nervy –

Jerry now taking time out to take shots of Freya just for the fun of it – the camera loves her, he says –

Emma, now holding the long headdress-veil up, out and away from Laura's blond curls, Freya reaching the rest of it up and out; so that a fixture involving a delicate silver tiara can be manipulated skilfully, by Julia the absolutely-punctual hairdresser, over newly-tweezed ringlets –

Bride's father again, now downstairs, masquerading as Captain Capable. He's ordered a few bottles of best bubbly, with attendant glassware arrayed on a long low table in the lounge, and here he welcomes the rest of the guests, with special smiles for some, as they arrive from their own hotel breakfasts, their own dressings-up ...

And then– they've all gathered ... and all ... gone.

The Groom's party, yes, everyone – including Jerry – and the bridesmaids.

Now literally unphotographable, the Captain's left to wait five or ten minutes before going to collect the bride from her room.

From his balcony, strangely attired in what really is period costume, he looks far out over a flawless bay to the jumble of Napoli, the lump that is Vesuvius.

* * *

"... dominant in every way, for sheer size, and the number of persons supporting the platform of images confronting the eruption, was that of San Sebastiano himself ...

"… We strolled back together into the main street, and in fact there had been no advance that I could detect in the last hour …

"… the day seemed to have lightened, and for a moment the sunlit cone of the volcano came into sight ahead, as if through a tear in a curtain. Childish voices in the rear had begun to sing a Te Deum. It seemed likely that half the town would be saved."

* * *

Now the Bride's be-ribboned silver limousine, he can see, is at the front steps.

He pings off another message to the Muse, knowing he'll soon have to turn off the phone …

Round mirrored corners of hotel corridors he's collected, from her room, The Bride – a bubbling vision of white, a glowing bunch of red roses held before her. He's helped her, and carefully collected up overflowing reams of The Dress, into The Car.

And minutes later, having been driven up a slight rise, he helps her again, and they step around the silver bonnet, cross a pavement …

Now, they're really not quite connected to the ground; giddy, leaning against each other next to railings high above a stupendously clear Bay of Naples. Everything else is so far away in haze, blinded in dazzle. So much shaken light. Here, three bridesmaids stand and smile, spaced like emerald angels, poised for the signal to process through a flickering avenue of trees to the open-air event that's just waiting round the corner. It'll be a walk of maybe a hundred yards. Is it a scene from a film? Like clockwork, the angels, bearing their own bouquets, begin to move.

Bride and father are saying the day is perfect, everything is beautiful, and other things they will later simply not remember.

Another signal: it's theirs. Check: he's at the correct side, her left: and they begin to walk. They approach the corner. She says, just a moment, and stops. Something maybe in her eye?

It's fortunate that somehow, each is carrying a tissue. She's just having a little moment, she says, it's all right. She carefully uses a corner of her tissue, then of his. "I don't want to smudge anything." They exchange a couple more, quiet words.

She draws herself up very straight. Takes a deep breath. OK.

You look amazing, Laura.

Thanks Dad.

From a discreet, invisible distance – it later transpires – the Muse's supernatural photographer has even caught that moment, too.

They start walking again, both backs now straightened. Twinkles, strains of a harp, begin to wander faintly to them on blue air....

Then – round the corner; and still thirty yards away, all the smiling faces are turned towards them. In perfect, 20-20 sunshine.

Chapter 42

The Final Push – up, up and away – traumatising the cattle – the post-War crew

The original plan had him meeting the Muse back at Tina and Bill's, next, and the two of them taking a few days in Tuscany together before getting back home for a bigger Wedding Reception. But an exchange of messages with her (and with Tina) has left that a poor second to his getting home as soon as possible.

Freya's already booked to fly back with Emma and Gordon. So in a late change of plan designed simultaneously to atone for all misdeeds real and imagined and to test himself to the limit, he's decided to drive, after the wedding, all the way back home before the weekend. From the wedding-hotel, sometime after first arrival, he'd already booked a ferry online, allowing him (more to the point, allowing dear Lotte) a steady three days to motor up to Zeebrugge: thence sailing to Hull, and speedily home. It'll be about 1800km, give or take, and the straightest line will take him all the way up Italy, through Genoa, through the Mont Blanc Tunnel, past Dijon, and north again from near Lille into Belgium, and thus to the ferry-port...

At the Wedding's afternoon-into-evening's party he'd said many affectionate, woozy, late goodbyes – and everybody understood (as well as they could – this strange man, so bizarre a method of arriving at, and of leaving, so important a life-event).

So this very next morning begins at 7.30, when he checks out, alone – and Lotte starts, of course, first time. She pulls eagerly away, no doubt to Emilia's lasting relief.

Oh. Look. Roads. Tarmac. White lines. Signs. Petrol stations. Once again, after so luminous a day, on a dull one, he's escaping a jammed, bollarded Salerno and the vortex of Naples by 9ish, and flogging north up the damned A30.

And in fact it's as if he has the devil driving him, or that he is driving down the devil. Lotte just nods like the willing beast of burden she is, and she goes and goes and goes. The note of those five experienced cylinders hardly changes all day....

At 5.30 the next morning, the Captain's delighted to hold the achievement, on waking from three and a half hours' sleep – that last night he made it *just* over to the French, return-side of the Alps. Now he lurches up out of his sleeping bag on the back bench-seat, and steps out into just-dawn on what he remembers as last night's two-hundred metre long pitch-black lay-by, in the lee of the big, silver petrol-tanker that pulled up behind him. He looks about to take his morning leak, and – smashed by last night's long climb and tunnel, by sleep and  still by white tulle and red roses – he has to gape and gasp – at a surrounding sugar-candy-tipped miracle of pink peaks. The homeward side of the great mountain barrier, and at this optimistic time of day, he wants to imagine them wishing him a rosily-sentimental farewell to Italy.

And a welcome again to France? "Paris" – it optimistically states on that sign – "622 km". At the same time, a bunch of young brown French cattle dozing together in a field the other side of the fence look up startled at his open-trousered effrontery. Easy to pee on your foot, in those circs.

He tanks up with coffee, and more diesel, and will drive, and pay his tolls, and drive, and try to fly....

223 Squadron had only a limited, if eventful, wartime life after Bob Connell's crew, Cyril included, were among a tranche of airmen rather belatedly released for home duty – after Cyril's 73 Ops, Bob's 78 – in January, 1944.[1]

Cliff the Aussie wireless-operator's war career after Italy isn't known to the Captain. Nor is Jack's. It's possible, though, that the crew continued dropping one another the odd line, at least at first.

Jack   Cyril   Bob   Cliff

Bob Connell was posted back to Egypt (by now a backwater-of-a-backwater of the war) as a pilot-instructor at OTU 70, at Shandur near Alexandria, and then to the UK. Despite being desperate to get back to Australia, where his parents and fiancée, Win, were anxiously waiting, he was still the RAF's property to do what they wanted with. He came to feel that "colonial" personnel, in particular, were regarded as expendable, certainly forgettable. The worst of it was that the old bomber-aircraft in which he now had to train his pilots were unreliable, patched-up old crates, maintained absent-mindedly at best: he watched gloomily, as it felt more fatalities than he'd seen in his shooting-war built up around him in this training unit. Worst of all, when his boys were put up in a ceremonial fly-past for, of all people, King

---

[1]   Continuing to follow the "line" northwards, the 223 Squadron they had left behind would go on to attack targets from Rome to Yugoslavia. More damage was done, more men were lost. At length they were disbanded, and their hardware mostly handed over, as Sqdrn 30 South African Air Force, to continue in the Mediterranean. By the end of the year, 223 Squadron RAF would be reconstituted back in England with new personnel, as a support unit mainly scattering "window" to confuse enemy radar and thus screen off the Bomber Command raids beyond D-Day.

Farouk of Egypt[2], two aircraft in the inexperienced, ramshackle formation collided. Ten young men were killed. And for what? he thought.

Posted to England in 1945, he found that this late-wartime Britain hadn't, in fact, despite the propaganda then and later, the "all in it together" sense of communal responsibility he'd shared with 223's rather piratical desert air- and ground-crew, in whose support he'd been able so implicitly to trust. He became deeply depressed, suddenly stopped writing home …

As for Cyril, he'd been recycled through various Training Units (and another hospital stay, to shake off more illness) to become a Gunnery Instructor. Now it appears that, earlier in the war, Bob must have asked for and been given Cyril's details for his folks back in New South Wales to contact "in case anything should happen". And so it was to him that they wrote, worried sick, from Australia in the spring of 1945 – how long would such a letter and its reply have taken, in war-time? Cyril himself had at first feared the worst. He had been thinking Bob *must* by now have sailed back Down Under, and so "I felt three months without a letter spelt Japanese torpedo in block capitals!"[3]

But he did succeed in getting hold of Bob again – discovering that he was still stuck in England, in a bad frame of mind. Contact with the Australian family, with a bit of encouragement, was able to be restored. And Bob probably also took up an invitation – there is a letter[4] suggesting it – to visit Cyril at his new posting in Lincolnshire. From which his old gunner-mate could go home to the missus on Saturdays! That must have been a real pisser.

And yet. And yet – though Cyril was going home to his war-bride Muriel, who would conceive their first child, Stephen, around this time – she was ill. Later on, Rosamond, two and a half years her brother's junior, was born in December 1947. But less than two years after that, Muriel died of cancer. (Her son would later become a modern languages teacher, then a civil servant; and her daughter, not two years old when she lost her mother, would grow up to be for thirty-odd years a nurse.)

---

2   – to persuade him, or maybe in recognition of his reluctant decision, with his arm up his back, to support the Allies in the war – for what that was worth at this stage. Farouk could occasionally turn a *bon mot*, allegedly ate 600 oysters a day, and was in fact a Nazi sympathiser. After his overthrow in a 1952 coup, he went into luxurious exile … in Italy.

3   Cyril: letter to Bob, August 1945. With thanks to Geoff and Kath Connell

4   Ibid

So four years after the war, Cyril had been left a widower with two children under five years old. At least he had a Council house …

… And two years later, he married again, to Muriel's former school-friend Mildred, and they moved into another house: with her mother. This was the family and the familial home into which, in 1951, the Captain was born, and six years later the final sibling, Brian.

And Bob? On return to his homeland he was married to Win – for seventy years, until they both died in their nineties. Bob and Cyril exchanged cards and wishes every Christmas, until Cyril's death in 1984.

Bob also retained contact, immediately after the war at least, with quiet English navigator-bomb-aimer, Jack … to send him food parcels.[5]

Chapter 43

Final lap – length of France – & roadsigns – stolen moments? –
acceptance & thankfulness – flashbacks – and back to the Main Event

And he decides: it's not out of the question to reach the ferry in – even better! – not three, but – two days.

Tanking up with still more coffee, still more diesel, he throws crisps in palate-blocking quantities into his mouth as he drives, drinks much more coffee and reaches the outskirts of Lille – by tea-time! It's rush-hour; but maybe he *can* just get that 7pm ferry, if he's only allowed to keep moving. That *would* be impressive. A whole day earlier than planned or expected! Yes!

But now, this must be said: he's sure the French are no worse in this next particular than certain other countries, but they are bad. The road signs that point the way northward away from the motoway westward to Lille do make mention of "Bruxelles" – to which the Captain has no wish to go today … and as he presses closer to Lille, he knows from the map there *is* a road north to Bruges, which *is* his route, and he therefore drives onward, waiting to see it named … but he has no navigator on his right-hand side, and soon, having passed up at least two routes north, which named only French places, in small print, whose names he doesn't recognize … pretty much immediately, he's *in* central Lille! That, he'd definitely intended to avoid …

It's only right that in the end, it's roads that have the last laugh on him.

The truth is: French road signs have told you, as soon as you came out of that tunnel in the Alps, just how ridiculously distant (but obviously irresistible) their marvellous Paris is from there, and told you that to the nearest kilometre; but they're reticent about telling you about anywhere, however nearby or arterial, *beyond their own borders*. That isn't, they seem to tell you, our job: our French road-signs will tell you how to get to tiny French villages on the road towards the border that leads to Bruges; but it was never our job to tell you, they seem to say, that it is also (and majorly) the road to that border, and to Bruges…

He curses them, and curses himself; but it's only his own tired old eyes and brain he's really cursing, and that's a waste of time.

He trundles gently on, to the ferry-port, arriving half an hour late. The ferry is probably only just out of sight.

But still … He's not really *late*, at all, he can tell himself. Late, but only for the ferry *before* the one he actually booked himself on … For which booking he is now heroically, magnificently, absurdly early. He'll spend the next twenty-three hours here now – it's an uninspiring spot, for sure – but he's content enough in the end to know that, a day early, he's done pretty much all his driving.

Done.

All.

His.

Driving.

He reads for a while, drinks several bottles of Peroni, and sleeps: and throughout the night the container-port crashes and hoots, bleeps and flashes its lights, rumbles its lorries through his head.

In the morning he watches the ferry that will take him home this evening, arriving in port to disgorge its traffic into Belgium. He stands and boils his kettle, watches heavy lorries, strings of cars, a couple of caravans, another motorhome – and even, gathering in cavalcade, a multicoloured convoy of old British Minis, intent no doubt on post-modernly emulating Michael Caine's 'Italian Job' – emerge, queue, pass along the quayside, and finally drift off the mental screen.

On this car-park, as it now starts at breakfast-time to fill once more, he measures his coffee-scoops, and suddenly is aware, as he's holding onto the mug: this feels like a stolen moment.

Stolen … moment …? At the end of five weeks' self-determined, often-solitary travel, a ….Stolen? … Moment?!

Finally? Now? On a ferry-port car park, at 8 in the morning, heading home?

Bitterly, he comes to know, he's felt like this on and off throughout the trip, though barely at the level of awareness. And it's terrible. As if he's *sneaked off*. As if some folks will feel it was all just a jolly jaunt, whatever he says. As if, when others reflect that about him, it's how he'll start to feel (and even now starts to feel) about himself. Like a furtive fag behind the bikesheds. Like a brief fling with a secretary (he's never had one of those. Why not?). Like….

Like? Not *like* anything.

A man nearing sixty, with plenty of well-earned later-life time on his hands; a daughter seen married; another blessed in her late pregnancy; the third having just shared a final trip away before she starts university. And home with the Muse tomorrow night after a mammoth drive. How could any man feel he needed to *steal moments* to do these things? After these rites and communions, how can he make himself feel that coffee on this car park, as his journey ends and those of a boat-load of others begin, is a *stolen* coffee? In a beat-up old van bought outright with his well-earned retirement pot, a coffee poured out of a second-hand kettle into a camping-mug – motorway milk added, and chewing the stale end of yesterday's Carrefour baguette? *Stolen?*

Ridiculous. But yes. Indeed. So it feels.

Worst of all, has the trip been *stolen* from the world? *Was* it the self-indulgent bucket-list trip of a carbon-burning baby-boomer? These vainglorious trips and drives? They've all been "for his own benefit". His generation are now, irreparably, "too big for their boots". Has he not Just Done It because He's Worth It?

This guilt is also the self-repressed gene of the man he had to take away on this trip. Back in Italy are pre-conceptual locations, places now once again left far behind. Now he'll always carry them as themselves. He has Shed Some Light On The Subject. The Dog Has Seen The Rabbit. It's Hard Lines for those live in times of war. Perhaps if anything is a seed of guilt to prise from between his teeth and spit out, that's it ...

In the end, all you can hope is that it's All For The Best.

But how come I'm here at all? Thanks, Bob, thanks Dad, for getting through it.

Having hoped in some way to lose him, to leave him behind, he did also find Cyril there again, no doubt about that. Every time he's said "Mersa Matruh", "Benghazi", "Brindisi", "Cassino", "Gerbini", "Etna", he's heard it uttered from that moustached mouth, rolled for years around a middle-aged nostalgic tongue, the old adventurism that shaped a Forties serviceman's sense of himself for the rest of his life. An occasional swagger of the lip, the pugilistic out-turn of the elbow, a savour of what had gone on, knowledge finally held in the paternal bone: I've been places, done things, know things... And what would have been the point, Dad, of knowing things you would rather not have learned, if you can't also obscurely hold them as a medal?

When they stood at that astonishing memorial in Randazzo, he'd found himself muttering words of regret for his father's war-work: of apology for acts committed by airmen in dismissive panic, hit-and-run against people and buildings it had been best not to know or to think about: labelled carefully "targets", "positions", "concentrations", "crossroads". But – people. People.

Most of us – the old man himself must have often reflected – most of us ordinary peaceful folk live in positions and concentrations near crossroads. That's what towns and villages *are*. And now and again in the news, still, we'll see the "minor collateral damage" of a little light bombing. It's not as if, afterwards they didn't know, those crews, even though they'd loyally never say it to those who'd never had it to do.

Now the Captain has learned it again *for* him, and somehow has therefore found himself prey to an arrested responsibility of his own, a transferred guilt. He only lives at all, has only carried forward those genes, through the "fate" that kept his father alive in that rattling, riveted turret – the same

Fate which, with the other hand, seeded death and deprivation among poor, beautiful mountains, towns, soldiers, citizens, families. The Captain's whole life, he feels then in one sense, was stolen; at gunpoint from the people of Italy, from the dead, from the never-to-be-conceived.

"*Stretching A Point*". Another one of Cyril's favourite phrases. Yet somehow it's with this knowledge he was sent to Sunday School. It's this learning that was reinforced in him by the War-decorated grammar-school Head (who also "didn't talk about it") whose morning prayer featured "We, whose lot is cast in so goodly a heritage".

In other words, "we" had no right to *expect* our heritage to be so goodly. We were not *entitled*. Deaths in War are never holy sacrifices, but always the heaviest cost, paid unwillingly, uncomprehendingly, and maybe in the end to benefit those who deserve life less. Benefit indirectly, but nonetheless.

Somewhere Else. Later.

The *future* is a foreign country. So, later, if your heritage is goodly, you must earn it retrospectively.

* * *

Message pings in from the Muse: "Wow that's amazing you've got there! Talk soon".

* * *

Dozing now a little, in the Belgian ferry-port, the Captain's for a moment again mentally stuck in Salerno – those blasted roadworks on the A3….

… Then, painlessly perusing a hazy view of Vesuvius, hazy prosecco-glass in hand, from the beautifully-laid table of wedding-feast veranda in Sorrento …

… Oh, and now the black-and-white ice-field, the moon-craters on top of Etna – bleached, scorched, streaked killer-whale of a mountain, under his feet and his daughter's, just as it had been under the mid-air falling-leaf terror of a spinning bomber and her crew, sixty-six and a half years before. Villainous cracks hiding in the rock, smoking grins ….

… and old men of Randazzo, between the back of their breeze-block-patched church and the public toilets. On their bench, top-trouser-buttons loosened; eyes glinting, mouths chuckling at him, smiling, greeting. And their piazza, and its eloquent, surreal memorial at which no local adult seemingly bothers, or can bear, to look any more – but up to which a little girl in her Brownie-style uniform stares with unfathomable love …

Now, at last, again, back in Sorrento. The ash-cloud did lift, then. The guests, even the last-minute photographer, all made it. Here they all are, with Vesuvius across the distance now just a hazy piece of Mediterranean seaside furniture to top off a stained-glass vision, a sweeping Bay of Naples. The weather wasn't good the last two days. But today, it's faultless. White Sorrento, turquoise waves, white boats, blue sky, dazzling sunlight, welcoming warmth of golden Mediterranean air.

In her hotel-room, his middle daughter waiting for him to collect her for the ceremony. A white vision. A glow. A bunch of deepest red roses.

Gasping, he does his best to speak (later he'll make a joke, of her pausing to neck the last of the *prosecco* before they go down) – Oh, but everything's welling up in him; and it's best just to stare, and gasp, and stare, and lead this beautiful, remarkable daughter of his: to the rest of the wedding-party, to her partner, to the Republican-green-white-and-red-sashed Registrar.

Down the stairs. Out into the glaring sun. In front, the wedding-Mercedes: blur of gleaming, fluttering ribbons. To his left on the forecourt, over old German Lotte's fixed grin, her big mirror flashes a wink.

Open-air ceremony. No altar, so no sacrifices. Not even a breath of breeze. Two other daughters, one pregnant, the other soon off to university, stand as bridesmaids, with the bride's best friend Sally: three, in vernal green. No volcanoes will erupt. Dad and daughter approach the bridegroom's side. There'll be no ashes. The sky that stares dazzlingly down is so clear, it can surely never have contained cloud, or a falling … anything.

Here we are. She loosens her grip on his arm. Heartbeats are deafening, difficult. The groom turns.

She lets go of her father's arm.

The only burst of flame is in his heart – and that – as he stands back, and she walks forward – that will surely burst.

Acknowledgements

Thanks to Clare, Paula and Duncan at YPS. The look and availability of this book after ten years' labour is also the fruit most recently of theirs.

Thanks to the Connell family of New South Wales, Australia: Thanks, Charlotte, for picking up out of the internet-ether my research-inquiries into 223 Squadron, Baltimores, and Bob Connell, pilot, your grandad. Thanks to the late Bob's son, the late Geoff ("Wuff"), and (ongoingly) Kath Connell – who ten years ago followed up, informed and encouraged me, and shared some ancient correspondence.

Thanks to Chris Clark for his encouragement and for his much more detailed work on Sdrns 55 and 223: "Rommel versus the Imperturbable Eighteen", Amazon.

I am grateful to Lavaglia editore and Comune di Eboli for their beautiful volume 'Eboli 1943-4 – Diario di una Donna'. I hope my translation of a passage from the book has done it some justice. I would like to see the whole book translated into English one day, and would gladly contribute if requested. Closer to home, thanks to Cecilia Vancheri for her help.

Like many researchers and writers I am greatly indebted if only in the first instance to Wikipedia, and I ain't too proud to praise the work of that cooperative enterprise to anyone who wants to listen.

I must thank Jerry Hardman-Jones for the use here of a couple of examples from his brilliant photographic record of the Sorrento wedding, and against all odds for getting there in the nick of time.

Finally, big thanks to "Pasetta" – Tomaso d'Amico – of Camping Gentiana, Barrea, whose positivity, energy, understanding and help – and whose book – were of such assistance to me at a crucial point. He represents all those of his country's folk who appreciated my interest in their history – and who encouraged me to look forward.

Other resources are acknowledged in footnotes. A full bibliography would take several pages, and I've chickened out.